Easy Type

ROS KINLOCH

```
x----------------------- x
i x                         x
i    x_____x
i    i                        i
i    i       EASY TYPE        i
i    i                        i
i    i   at   at   at   at   at   at i
i    i  sat sat sat sat sat sat i
i    i  rat rat rat rat rat rat i
 x   i  hat hat hat hat hat hat i
   x i                        i
     x_____x
```

```
 _____
|
|   E         QWERTYUIOP          T
|     A       ASDFGHJKL;          Y
 \     S      ZXCVBNM,.?          P
  \     Y     _____        E
   \       ---------------------------------
           ---------------------------------
```

EGON

EGON PUBLISHERS LTD
Royston Road, Baldock, Hertfordshire SG7 6NW, England

First published in the United Kingdom in 1994
Second impression 1995
Third impression 1997
Fourth impression 2001
by Egon Publishers Ltd
Royston Road, Baldock, Hertfordshire SG7 6NW, England

ISBN 0 905858 90 5

Printed by Streets Printers, Royston Road, Baldock, Hertfordshire SG7 6NW, England

ACKNOWLEDGEMENTS

I would like to take the opportunity to thank The Lynn Lewis Holiday School for first making me aware of the potential and importance of teaching keyboard skills to children with learning difficulties.

I am also indebted to St Andrew's Hospital, Northampton, for allowing me time and facilities to develop this project. In particular, I would like to thank Rawdon Walker, Director of Education at St Andrew's, for his support, encouragement and unfailing confidence in the "Easy Type" project.

Ros Kinloch
April 1994

EASY TYPE – TEACHER'S NOTES

A DUAL PURPOSE – SPELLING AND KEYBOARD DEVELOPMENT

The Easy Type manual came about as a result of the computer revolution. As computer systems became widely available in schools and homes, so word processing started to offer students a more flexible alternative to hand written communication. Within the Special Needs sector, the potential of word processing began to be recognised. Here was a medium that could offer real support and an improved performance for students with learning difficulties. But when word processing kit was made available to SN students, they did not always find it as helpful as they had first hoped. The kit was tried for a while, but was all too often abandoned and left to gather dust in drawers.

This is still often the position today, and a large part of the problem seems to lie in a lack of training of the individual students in 1) how to operate the kit, and 2) how to use the keyboard efficiently. The Easy Type manual does not address the first problem – word processing kit – it is too diverse for one manual to achieve this. But it does aim to address the second and teach keyboard skills and build keyboard familiarisation. If keyboard skills are not taught, then the inputting of material can be a slow and arduous task, and the word processor can become as frustrating as the pen to the SN student.

However the Easy Type manual aims to do more than just teach keyboard skill. It recognises the potential for a keyboard course to also work on spelling development. So by devising material based on phonics, word family patterns and high frequency spellings, it has been possible to link in a strong spelling aspect to the work of building keyboard skills.

EASY TYPE – THE USER GROUP – STUDENTS AND TEACHERS

Easy Type has been tested successfully in a wide range of Special Needs educational settings; in mainstream schools, in special schools and units

and in the Adult Basic Educational environment. It has proved successful with different types of learning difficulties and although it was originally designed with the dyslexic learner in mind, the wider scope of the material has been recognised. So in addition to the dyslexic population, it has proved a useful programme with slow learners, with students having emotional and behavioural difficulties and with some students with motor and physical handicaps. It has been used for Year 3 children, through Secondary age groups up into all adult ranges.

Teachers using "Easy Type" do not need typing qualifications or skills. The material is self explanatory and you can learn alongside your students. It needs special needs skills to teach it, not typing skills.

WORD PROCESSING – A MULTI-PLUS MEDIUM FOR SN STUDENTS

Word Processing has many advantages, particularly for students experiencing difficulties with writing and spelling. The benefit package includes:

- **Motivation/concentration**

  It is a Hi-Tech activity which allows students to work through a computer based medium, where particularly in the case of dyslexics, they may be high achievers.

- **Reduces letter confusions**

  The keyboard is in CAPITALS and this makes it easier for the student to discriminate between, for example, "b" and "d", and "u" and "n". It also reduces any inappropriate use of capital letters – once set in lower case, the keyboard stays in lower case.

- **Helps directional awareness**

  Typed letters move consistently in a left–right movement and have no difficulties of direction! The line "wrap" or RETURN functions also relieve pressure on students who have difficulty making the manoeuvre from the end of one line to the beginning of the next.

- **Removes line and spacing problems.**

  Many SN students have difficulties spacing out their words, the letters within words and keeping their work in a straight line. All these problems vanish with a word processor.

- **Alternative to handwriting**

  Typing offers an alternative and very legible system of written communication for the student whose handwriting maybe untidy, illegible and laborious. Particular difficulties experienced by left handers in writing are not a problem on the

keyboard. Typing shares the load out equally between the two hands.

- Speed and presentation

Once keyboard skills are learned, the extra speed alone is a very real benefit. Tidy, well presented work is another.

- Motor skills, coordination and rhythm

The development of keyboard skills helps build fine motor control and hand coordination. The "Easy Type" material, with its emphasis on 4 beat warm up drills, also helps build a sense of rhythm.

- Spelling and proof reading

Spell checkers help alert SN students to errors and offer solutions. Proof reading is encouraged by the ease and invisibility of making corrections. The "Easy Type" material also builds spelling awareness.

HARDWARE, SOFTWARE AND FONT CHOICE

The "Easy Type" material can be used on any computer system and with any word processing package. It has been widely used on the BBC, Nimbus and Archimedes systems, as well as a variety of lap tops. It has been used with word processing software that includes Word, First Word Plus, Write, Caxton and Impression. It can also be used with conventional electric and manual typewriters. Indeed manual typewriters sometimes offer the best way in for children experiencing gross motor difficulties, because they do not require the fine motor skills of an electronic keyboard to control. Editing and display work on these machines is, of course, less satisfactory.

A choice of fonts and font sizes is useful to encourage the student to experiment with different type faces, to achieve visual variety and to learn how to access in different styles. In order to easily achieve the pictures in the material (eg. the ladders, flags and shapes) it is helpful to have an equidistant shaped font – ie: a font where each letter takes up exactly the same amount of space. "Courier" is an example of an equidistant font. Without this, the shapes loose regularity. The instructions

for the picture pages are based on an equidistant font choice. Within the manual, the CENTRE, BOLD and TAB functions are used from time to time, and it is helpful, though not necessary to have these available. Instruction in their use must be given.

THE "EASY TYPE" MATERIAL

"Easy Type" contains four modules. The first one works on the Home Key letters. The second tackles the Top Row letters. The third develops skills on the Bottom Row, while the fourth module has two uses. It can either be used as consolidation and overlearning material or can be used as a simple, easy start package for those having difficulties handling the mainly 3–4 letter sequences demanded by the other modules. The Consolidation Module is very small step, and keeps the typing task to 2 letter sequences, building consonant and vowel familiarity. The material features:

- Tick off recording sheets (photocopiable) providing easy evidence of work completed.
- Hand maps as a visual support to help the student match up and organise his hands and fingers over the keyboard.
- Photocopiable theory pages, where students have to fill in the letters onto hand maps.
- Pictures to type (ladders, flags, trees, shapes), which are motivational and give excellent practice in editing skills and cursor movement.
- Clear instructions on each page.
- "Bubbles" giving hints, reminders and reading practice.

HINTS ON USING THE "EASY TYPE" MATERIAL

1: "Easy Type" conforms to the Special Need principles of being small stepped, tightly structured, cumulative, overlearned and multi-sensory. But it can only be fully multi-sensory if taught in this way.

   a) FEEL: Typing is a very kinaesthetic, touch based action. The student

experiences the feel of the word and learns its movement through the repeated patterns. The four beat rhythmic drills are important for drumming in a regular touch pattern. It is also sometimes helpful to practice the finger action and establish the movement for the drill on the table, or on the page's hand map, before trying it on the keyboard.

b) VISUAL: The student sees his work coming onto the screen. He sees the letters on the keyboard. (NB. Touch typing is by no means encouraged – if a student needs to look at the keyboard, then that is fine, but he does need to learn to keep a close eye on the screen as well.) Also it is very useful, particularly in the early sessions, to ink up the student's fingers with the appropriate letters. In this way he can match the letter on his fingers to those on the keyboard.

c) AUDITORY: Unless the technology of a "talk back" system is being used, where the computer will name the words typed, the auditory input needs to be provided by either the teacher, the student or both. To do this the student needs to be instructed in Simultaneous Oral Typing techniques, where he names the letters and spaces as he types them. As with simultaneous oral spelling, this helps to keep concentration in place and the spelling sequence intact.

2: It is useful to do some introductory assessment work with each child starting the course. Pages 2, 3 and 7 of the manual are useful for this assessment. Page 2, where the student simply has to use each finger, one by one, will show you how efficient each finger is and give some insight into levels of coordination and fine motor control. Many students experience initial difficulty controlling their little fingers, but control often builds with surprising ease. Page 3 tests the student's control on two letter sequences, coordinating both hands together. Again initial difficulties are often quickly overcome and rapid improvement made. Page 7 extends the student to three and four letter sequences. Most will cope with this quite well and can progress through the manual in the normal way. If difficulties at this level persist, then it may be worth moving straight to Module Four of "Easy

Type" and working through this first, as it can be used as an easy start programme, keeping the task to only two letter chunks. The material is designed to be flexible. Pages can be used out of order to suit, and there may be good reasons to skip some of the exercises.

3: Instructions are given on each page, and often relate to "all the Two's". This particularly applies to the two letter and warm up drills, where the idea is to establish a strong 4 beat momentum, giving energy and flow to the work. Where the sequence is more than two letters, please use the normal one space between words. The manual suggests that each drill is typed for two lines. This however is based on a large font, perhaps of size 35+. If you use a smaller sized font, then one line may be quite sufficient. It is important however to encourage the student to go for perfection and edit out any errors that occur. Invisible and flexible editing is one of the major advantages of word processing and students must become competent in editing techniques, if they are to use the medium to its full potential.

4: To get full linguistic benefit from the material it is important to discuss the blend, word, phrase or sentence with the student and make sure he can read the material. Some of the bubbles give extra practice by putting the words into a sentence context. At the end of the page, when the student has completed the keyboard work, it is often useful to use the words as a spelling probe and dictation, to check that the spelling has been absorbed.

5: A good hand and sitting position needs to be encouraged if good keyboard skills are going to be learned. The "best" sitting position for most seems to be with the bottom pushed to the back of the chair, and a straight back, tilted slightly forward. The hand position is very important. Many students will slump their hands low on the keyboard, resting their wrists on the table, and tucking their thumbs down the front of the keyboard. They need to be taught the "Hovercraft Hands" technique to get good movement over the keyboard. The hovercraft analogy may help them realise that hands sunk into the keyboard go

more slowly than ones hovering above. The thumbs MUST be positioned over the space bar.

AND FINALLY!

"Easy Type" has been through a stringent process of trialling, re-trialling, adapting and adjustment, until hopefully it has achieved a high standard, special needs keyboard and spelling package. I do hope it proves valuable in your teaching/learning situation and that the material will be both beneficial and enjoyable to use. Good luck with "Easy Type".

Ros Kinloch
April 1994

Part One

THE HOME KEYS MODULE

CONTENTS

Use the Contents Page as a Record Sheet. Tick off the pages you have done in the boxes on the right.

PART ONE – THE HOME KEYS MODULE

HOME KEYS FINGER CHART

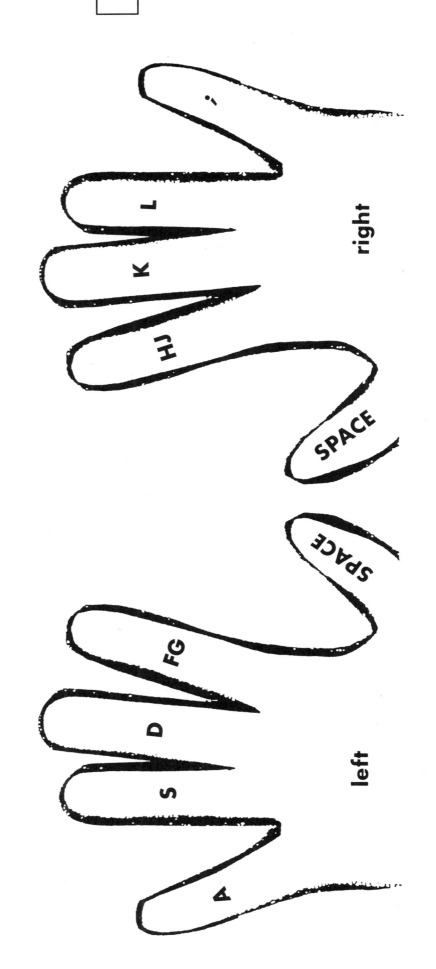

GET TO KNOW THE HOME KEYS

WHAT TO DO: This page takes a look at the Home Keys. Use the chart to find the right fingers, then type each exercise - TWO letters, TWO spaces. TWO lines - as in the sample.

SAMPLE: ("AA" SPACE SPACE)

aa   aa   aa   aa   aa   aa   aa   aa   aa   aa

aa   aa   aa   aa   aa   aa   aa   aa   aa   aa

1. AA
2. ;;
3. SS
4. LL
5. DD
6. KK
7. FF
8. JJ
9. GG
10. HH

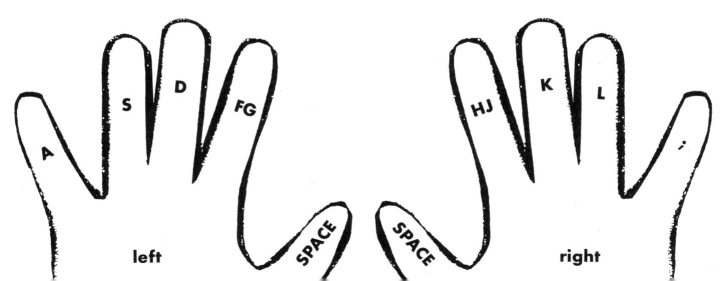

left   right

HOME KEYS
CONSONANT BLENDS

WHAT TO DO: All the TWOs - TWO letters, TWO spaces, TWO lines, to make a strong 4-beat rhythm.

SAMPLE: ("SH" SPACE SPACE)

sh sh sh sh sh sh sh sh sh sh sh sh
sh sh sh sh sh sh sh sh sh sh sh sh

1. sh
2. sk
3. sl
4. fl
5. gl
6. lk
7. lf
8. ld

N.B. "l" is a lower case "L", not "I".

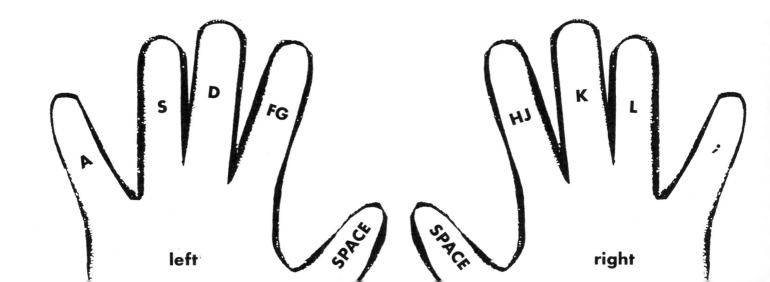

left   right

HOME KEY ROW
HAND COORDINATION EXERCISE
"Both Hands Together!"

WHAT TO DO: Type each exercise for TWO lines, with TWO spaces between the letters, to get a strong 4-beat rhythm.

SAMPLE: (AA SPACE SPACE ;; SPACE SPACE)

aa   ;;   aa   ;;   aa   ;;   aa   ;;   aa   ;;   aa   ;;

aa   ;;   aa   ;;   aa   ;;   aa   ;;   aa   ;;   aa   ;;

1. AA   ;;
2. SS   LL
3. DD   KK
4. FF   JJ
5. GG   HH

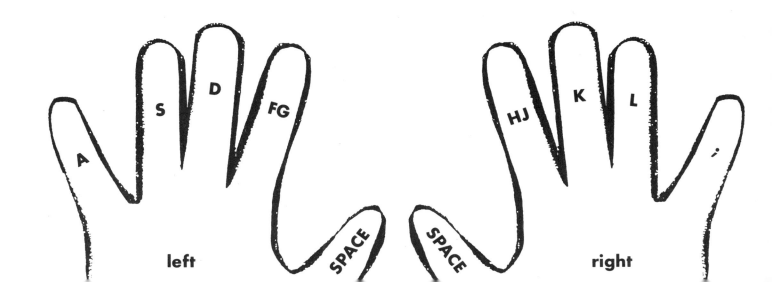

HOME KEYS
Little Finger Press Ups!

WHAT TO DO: This page will help strengthen up your little fingers. Type each drill for TWO lines with TWO spaces, as in the sample.

SAMPLE: (A; SPACE SPACE)

a; a; a; a; a; a; a; a; a; a; a; a;

a; a; a; a; a; a; a; a; a; a; a; a;

This page will make your little fingers ache!

1. A;
2. AL
3. S;
4. AK
5. D;
6. AJ
7. F;
8. AH
9. G;

But not for long They'll soon be strong!

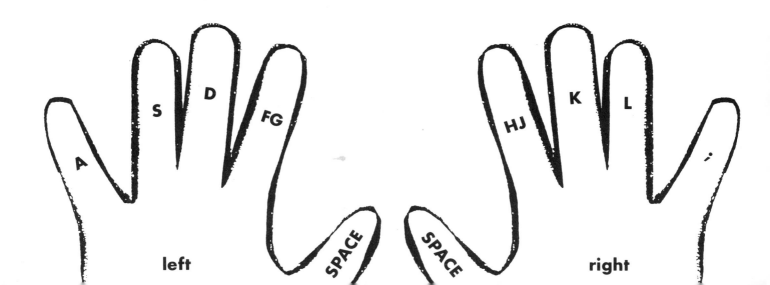

left   SPACE   SPACE   right

HOME KEYS
THE "AD" GROUP

WHAT TO DO: Check the finger chart, then type each word as many times as you can for TWO lines. Put ONE space between the words, but use TWO spaces on the Warm Up exercise to get a 4-beat rhythm.

WARM UP: ("AD" SPACE SPACE)

ad ad ad ad ad ad ad ad ad ad
ad ad ad ad ad ad ad ad ad ad

Keep your hands hovering above the keyboard.

1. lad
2. sad
3. had
4. dad
5. gad
6. glad

Dad was glad he saw the lad.

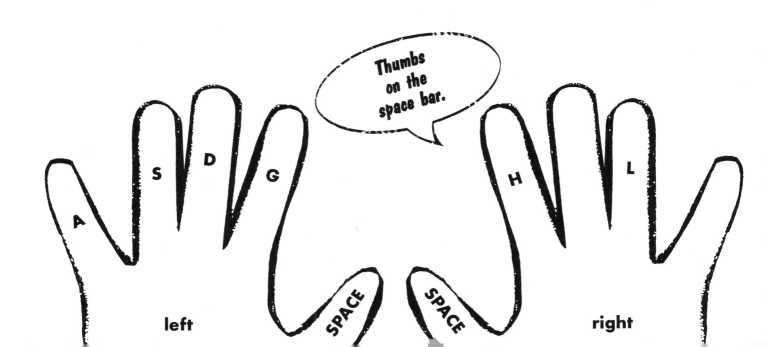

Thumbs on the space bar.

left   right

7

HOME KEYS
THE "AG" GROUP

WHAT TO DO: Check the fingering and then type each word — TWO lines per word — with ONE space between each word. Use TWO spaces in the WARM UP exercise to get a strong 4 beat rhythm.

WARM UP: ("AG" SPACE SPACE)

ag   ag   ag   ag   ag   ag   ag   ag   ag   ag
ag   ag   ag   ag   ag   ag   ag   ag   ag   ag

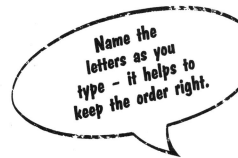

1. lag
2. hag
3. sag
4. gag
5. fag
6. flag

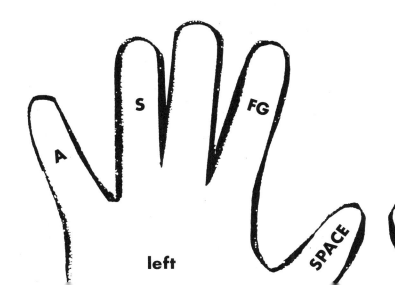

left

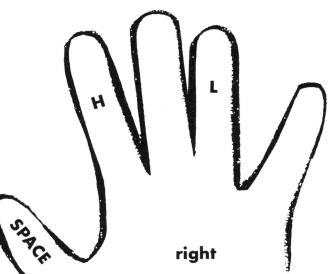

right

8

HOME KEYS
THE "AS" GROUP

WHAT TO DO: Type each word as many times as you can for TWO lines per word. Put in ONE space after each word, apart form the WARM UP, where you use TWO spaces.

WARM UP: ("AS" SPACE SPACE)

as   as   as   as   as   as   as   as   as   as   as

as   as   as   as   as   as   as   as   as   as   as

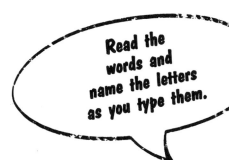

1. has
2. gas
3. ass
4. lass
5. glass

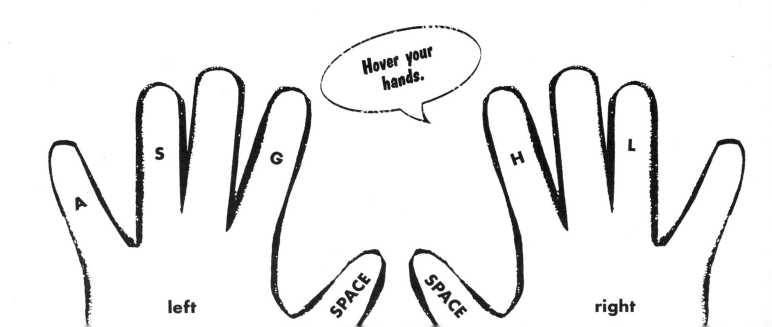

9

HOME KEYS
THE "ALL" GROUP

WHAT TO DO: First check the fingering. Then do the 4 beat WARM UP. Then type each word — TWO lines and ONE space between the words.

WARM UP: ("AL" SPACE SPACE)

al al al al al al al al al al al al
al al al al al al al al al al al al

Don't let your wrists rest on the keyboard - hover your hands.

1. all
2. hall
3. halls
4. fall
5. falls
6. shall

We shall all fall over on this new hall floor.

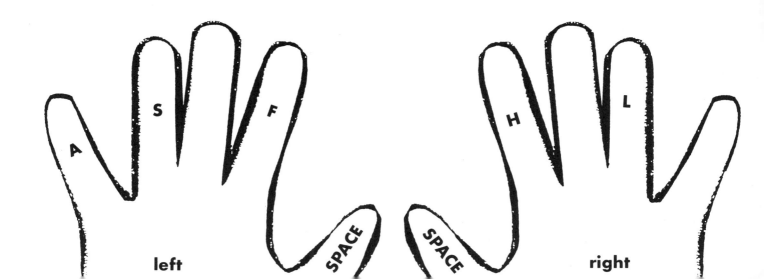

left   right

10

HOME KEYS
THE "SH" GROUP

WHAT TO DO: Check the finger chart. Do the 4 beat WARM UP (TWO spaces), then type each word TWO lines per word with ONE space between them.

WARM UP: ("SH" SPACE SPACE)

sh   sh   sh   sh   sh   sh   sh   sh   sh   sh   sh   sh
sh   sh   sh   sh   sh   sh   sh   sh   sh   sh   sh   sh

1. ash
2. dash
3. lash
4. sash
5. gash
6. hash
7. slash
8. flash

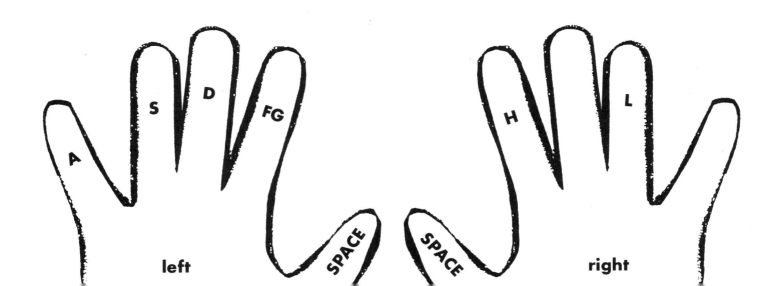

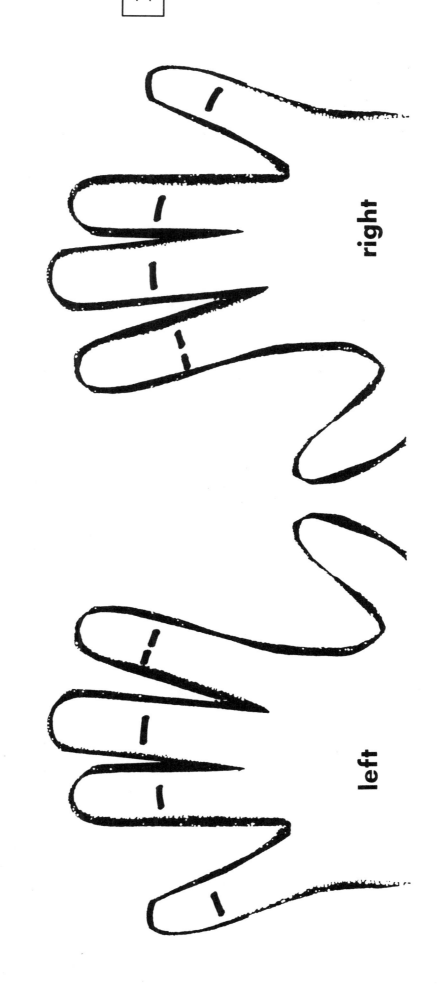

THEORY CHART
FILL IN THE HOME KEYS

left

right

HOME KEYS
PHRASE BUILDING

WHAT TO DO: Either type each phrase as many times as you can for ONE line as in the sample.

SAMPLE: a lad a lad a lad a lad a lad a lad a lad

OR copy the layout below exactly, making sure the numbers and words line up.

WARM UP: ("A" SPACE)

a a a a a a a a a a a a a a a a a a a a

Say the words as you type them.

1. a lad
2. a glad lad
3. a dad
4. a glad dad
5. all lads
6. all glad lads
7. all dads
8. all glad dads

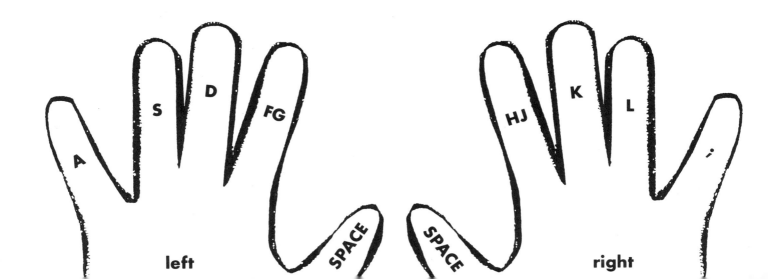

13

HOME KEYS
SIMPLE PHRASES WITH "AS"

WHAT TO DO: Either type each phrase as many times as you can for ONE line, as in the sample.

SAMPLE: as sad as as sad as as sad as as sad as

OR lay out the phrases exactly as below, making sure the numbers and columns line up.

WARM UP: ("AS" SPACE SPACE)

as   as   as   as   as   as   as   as   as   as   as

Say the words as you type them.

1. as sad as
2. as glad as
3. as a lad
4. as a dad
5. as a flag
6. as all lads
7. as all dads
8. as all flags

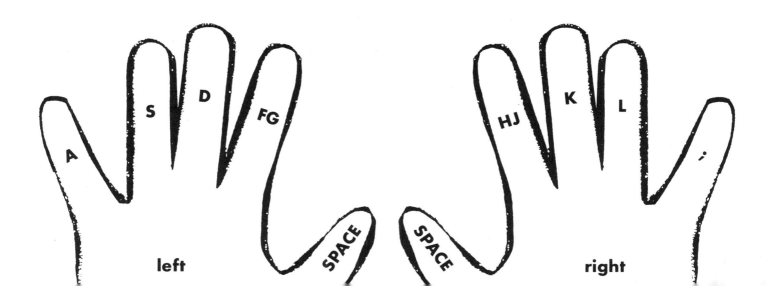

left   right

14

HOME KEY COLUMNS

WHAT TO DO: Copy the exercise below. Hold down the SHIFT key to get CAPITALS. Use TABS for the columns — your teacher will show you how to work the TABS.

CAPS	SMALL
A	a
S	s
D	d
F	f
G	g
H	h
J	i
K	k
L	l

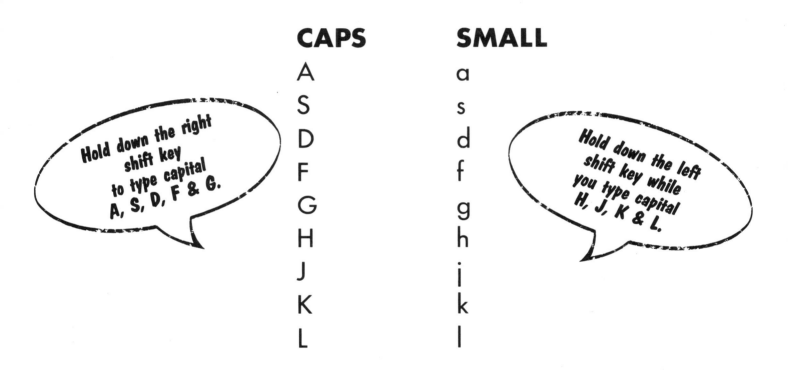

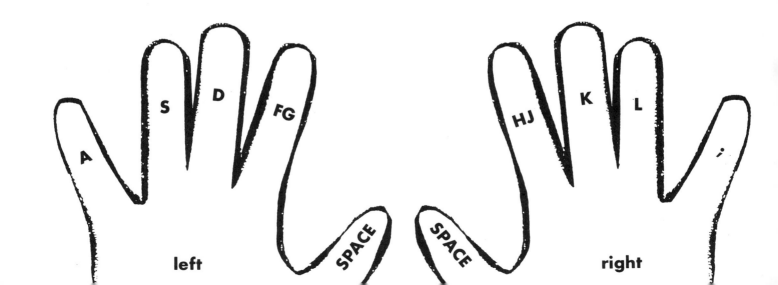

left   right

15

SENTENCE BUILDING — HOME KEYS

WHAT TO DO: Copy the exercises as they are shown below. Use a CAPITAL letter to start each line. Don't forget the FULL STOP on the last line.

A. Dad
   Dad shall
   Dad shall fall.

B. All
   All flags
   All flags sag.

Hold down the shift key to type a capital letter.

C. A
   A lad
   A lad shall
   A lad shall flag.

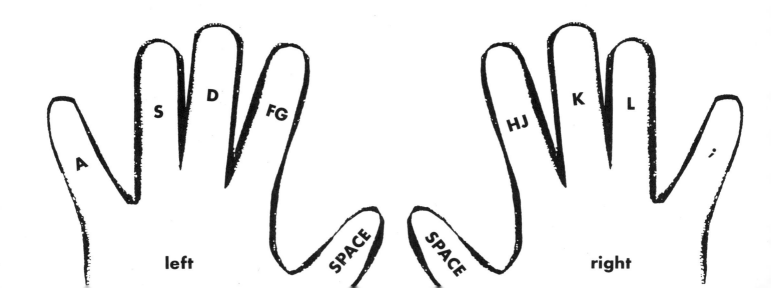

16

MAKING SHAPES
HOME KEY TRIANGLES

WHAT TO DO: Check your fingering on the Home Keys. Then copy the triangles below, using the CENTRING FUNCTION on your word processor to make the shape. The numbers you need are written down the right-hand side. You will need an equidistant font (see Teacher's Notes Font Choice) to make the shape work.

LOWER CASE TRIANGLE

```
                    aa                          aa  x   1
                ;;    ;;                        ;;  x   2
                ss  ss  ss                      ss  x   3
              ll  ll  ll  ll                     ll  x   4
            dd  dd  dd  dd  dd                   dd  x   5
          kk  kk  kk  kk  kk  kk                 kk  x   6
        ff  ff  ff  ff  ff  ff  ff               ff  x   7
      ii  ii  ii  ii  ii  ii  ii  ii             ii  x   8
    gg  gg  gg  gg  gg  gg  gg  gg  gg           gg  x   9
  hh  hh  hh  hh  hh  hh  hh  hh  hh  hh         hh  x  10
```

UPPER CASE TRIANGLE

Lock into capitals for the upper case triangle.

```
                    AA                          AA  x   1
                ;;    ;;                        ;;  x   2
                SS  SS  SS                      SS  x   3
              LL  LL  LL  LL                     LL  x   4
            DD  DD  DD  DD  DD                   DD  x   5
          KK  KK  KK  KK  KK  KK                 KK  x   6
        FF  FF  FF  FF  FF  FF  FF               FF  x   7
      II  II  II  II  II  II  II  II             II  x   8
    GG  GG  GG  GG  GG  GG  GG  GG  GG           GG  x   9
  HH  HH  HH  HH  HH  HH  HH  HH  HH  HH         HH  x  10
```

17

MAKING SHAPES
HOME KEY DIAMOND

WHAT TO DO: Check your HOME Key fingering. Copy the Diamond shape below using your CENTRING FUNCTION to get each line in the right position. Notice that the middle line is in **BOLD PRINT** so find out how the use your BOLD command. The number of times you need to type each key is written down the right-hand side of the page. You will need an equidistant font (see Teacher's Notes) to make the diamond work.

```
                    AA                          AA  x   1

                  ;;  ;;                        ;;  x   2

                SS  SS  SS                       SS  x   3

              LL  LL  LL  LL                     LL  x   4

            DD  DD  DD  DD  DD                    DD  x   5

          KK  KK  KK  KK  KK  KK                  KK  x   6

        FF  FF  FF  FF  FF  FF  FF                FF  x   7

      II  II  II  II  II  II  II  II              II  x   8

    GG  GG  GG  GG  GG  GG  GG  GG  GG            GG  x   9

  HH  HH  HH  HH  HH  HH  HH  HH  HH  HH          HH  x  10

    GG  GG  GG  GG  GG  GG  GG  GG  GG            GG  x   9

      II  II  II  II  II  II  II  II              II  x   8

        FF  FF  FF  FF  FF  FF  FF                FF  x   7

          KK  KK  KK  KK  KK  KK                  KK  x   6

            DD  DD  DD  DD  DD                    DD  x   5

              LL  LL  LL  LL                     LL  x   4

                SS  SS  SS                       SS  x   3

                  ;;  ;;                        ;;  x   2

                    AA                          AA  x   1
```

(Bold)

18

MAKING SHAPES
HOME KEY LADDER

WHAT TO DO: Copy the ladder below, which is made from the Home Key letters. Use TABS to position each upright. You will need an equidistant font (see Teacher's Notes) to make the ladder work.

Find out how to use the tabs and try and get the ladder across the middle of the page.

```
;;                    ;;
;;AAAAAAAAAA;;
;;LLLLLLLLLL;;
;;SSSSSSSSSS;;
;;DDDDDDDDDD;;
;;KKKKKKKKKK;;
;;FFFFFFFFFF;;
;;JJJJJJJJJJ;;
;;GGGGGGGGGG;;
;;HHHHHHHHHH;;
;;                    ;;
;;                    ;;
```

HOME KEY FLAG

WHAT TO DO: Copy the flag below, which is made from the Home keys. Use your TAB key to position your flag on the page. An equidistant font makes a better shape.

```
;;;AAAAAAAAAAAAAAAAAAAAAA
;;;LLLLLLLLLLLLLLLLLLLLL
;;;SSSSSSSSSSSSSSSSSSS
;;;DDDDDDDDDDDDDDDDD
;;;KKKKKKKKKKKKKKK
;;;FFFFFFFFFFFFFFFFF
;;;JJJJJJJJJJJJJJJJJJJJ
;;;GGGGGGGGGGGGGGGGGGGG
;;;HHHHHHHHHHHHHHHHHHHHHHHH
;;;
;;;
;;;
;;;
;;;
;;;
;;;
```

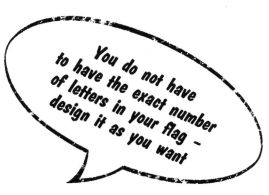

You do not have to have the exact number of letters in your flag – design it as you want

Part Two

TOP ROW MODULE

CONTENTS

Use the Contents Page as a Record Sheet. Tick off the pages you have done in the boxes on the right.

PART TWO – TOP ROW MODULE

TOP ROW

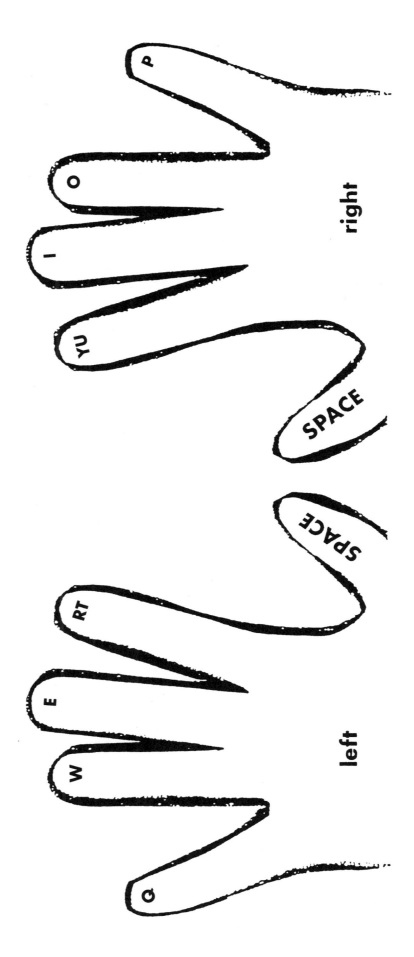

TOP ROW
Fill in the Home Keys

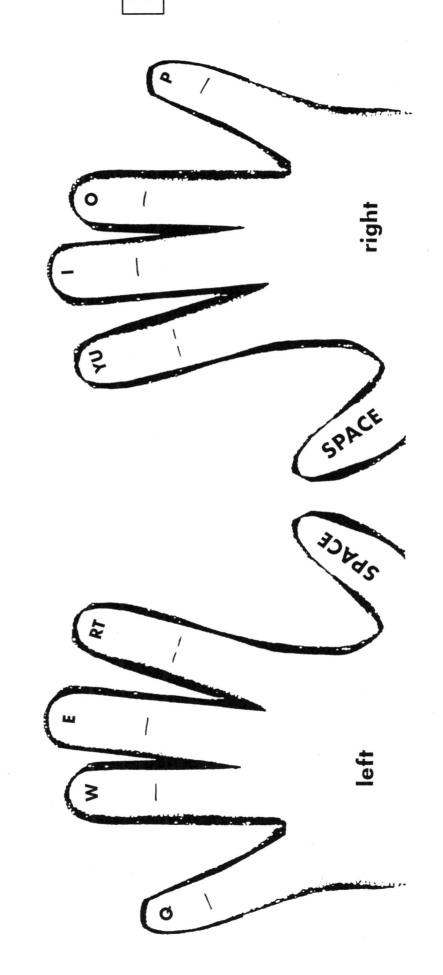

LEARN THE TOP ROW
TEN NEW LETTERS!

WHAT TO DO: Look at the chart. Put your fingers on the HOME KEYS and then move them up to the TOP ROW. Type each letter TWICE with TWO spaces and for TWO lines.

Delete errors. Keep your work looking good.

SAMPLE: ("QQ" SPACE SPACE)

qq qq qq qq qq qq qq qq qq qq qq qq
qq qq qq qq qq qq qq qq qq qq qq qq

Move your hands up and down between the home keys and top row.

1. QQ
2. PP
3. WW
4. OO
5. EE
6. II
7. RR
8. UU
9. TT
10. YY

You now know all the vowels - a, e, i, o + u

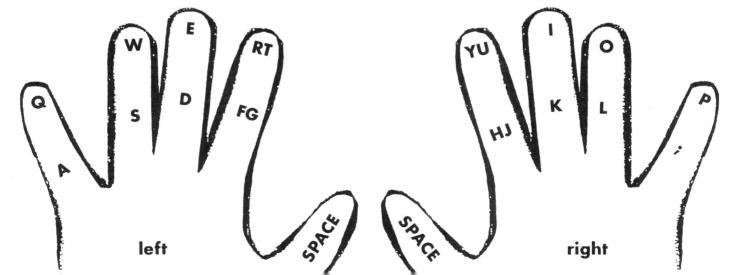

22

"GOING UP!"
HOME KEY TO TOP ROW

WHAT TO DO: Make sure the same finger types the two letters in the drill. Type ALL THE TWOs - TWO letters, TWO spaces, TWO lines, as in the sample.

SAMPLE: ("AQ" SPACE SPACE)

aq aq aq aq aq aq aq aq aq aq aq aq aq aq
aq aq aq aq aq aq aq aq aq aq aq aq aq aq

Try and keep a strong 4-beat rhythm going.

1. AQ ——————— Little fingers
2. ;P
3. SW ——————— 4th Fingers
4. LO
5. DE ——————— 3rd Fingers
6. KI
7. FR
8. JU ——————— Index fingers
9. GT
10. HY

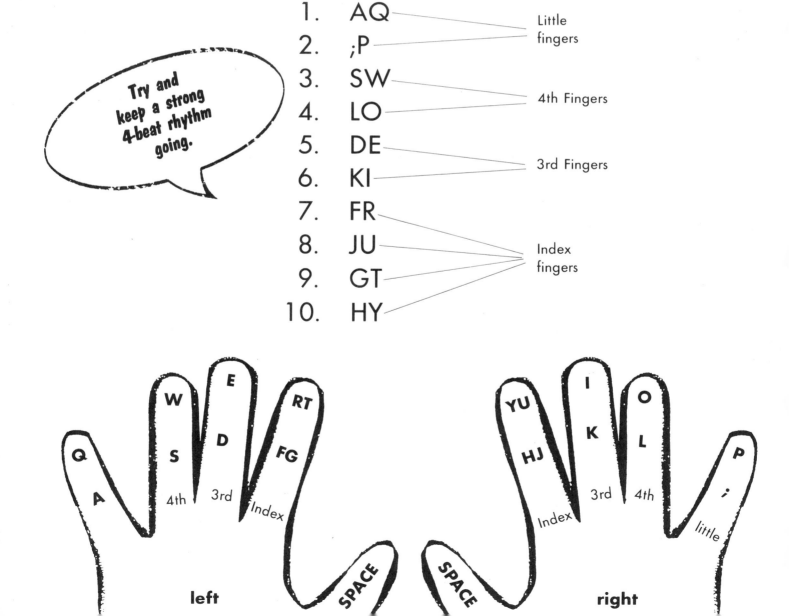

23

"GOING DOWN!"
TOP ROW TO HOME KEYS

WHAT TO DO: Make sure that the same finger types each drill. Type TWO letters, for TWO spaces and for TWO lines as in the sample.

SAMPLE: ("QA" SPACE SPACE)

qa qa qa qa qa qa qa qa qa qa qa qa qa qa
qa qa qa qa qa qa qa qa qa qa qa qa qa qa

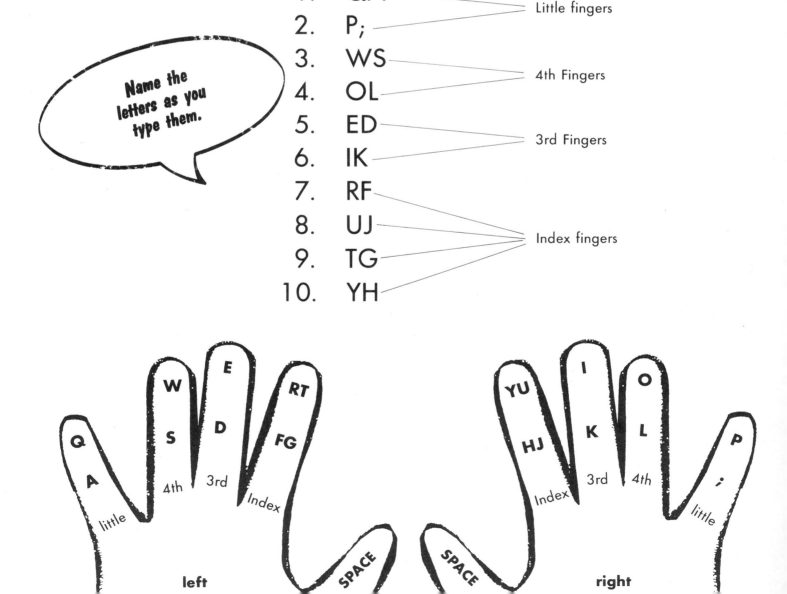

1. QA — Little fingers
2. P; — Little fingers
3. WS — 4th Fingers
4. OL — 4th Fingers
5. ED — 3rd Fingers
6. IK — 3rd Fingers
7. RF — Index fingers
8. UJ — Index fingers
9. TG — Index fingers
10. YH — Index fingers

Name the letters as you type them.

CONSONANT BLENDS
HOME KEYS AND TOP ROW

WHAT TO DO: Read the blends. Then check your fingering on the chart before you type each blend - TWO letters, TWO spaces, TWO rows.

SAMPLE: ("TR" SPACE SPACE)

tr tr tr tr tr tr tr tr tr tr tr tr tr tr tr tr tr tr tr tr
tr tr tr tr tr tr tr tr tr tr tr tr tr tr tr tr tr tr tr tr

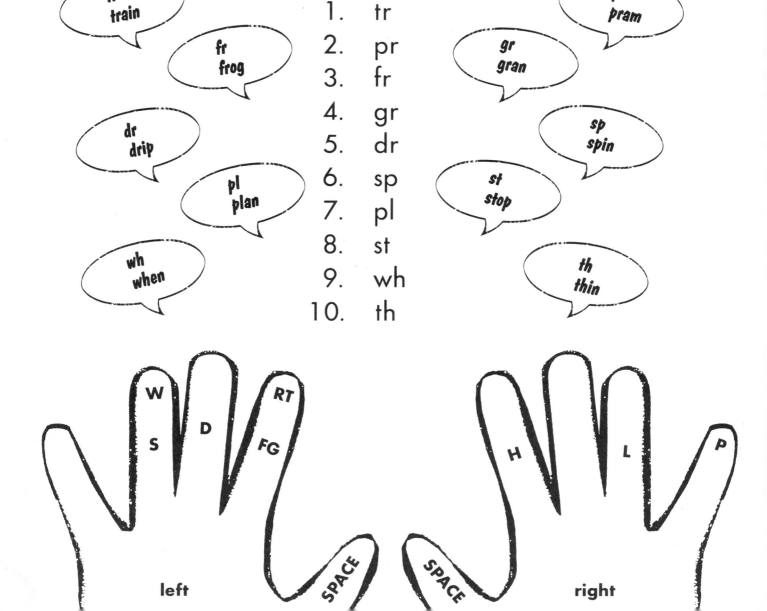

tr train
fr frog
dr drip
pl plan
wh when

1. tr
2. pr
3. fr
4. gr
5. dr
6. sp
7. pl
8. st
9. wh
10. th

pr pram
gr gran
sp spin
st stop
th thin

left   right

25

FINAL "L" BLENDS
HOME KEY AND TOP ROWS

WHAT TO DO: On this page there are two letter blends and words using those blends. Put TWO spaces after the blends to make a 4 beat drill, but only ONE space after the words.

WARM UP: ("LL" SPACE SPACE)

|| || || || || || || || || || || || || || || || || || || || || || || || ||
|| || || || || || || || || || || || || || || || || || || || || || || || ||

1.   lt
2.   salt
3.   lp
4.   help
5.   ld
6.   sold
7.   lk
8.   silk
9.   lf
10. wolf

Make sure you can read the blends and the words.

I sold some silk and salt to buy the wolf.

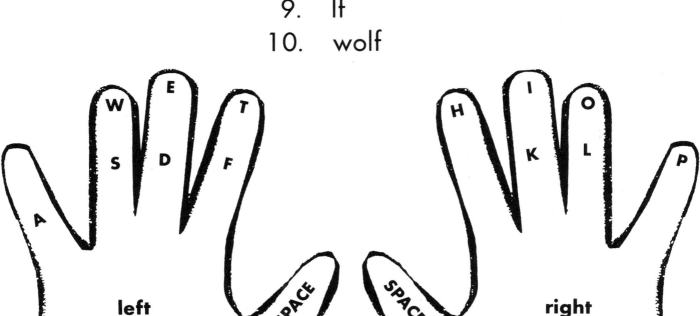

left   SPACE   SPACE   right

26

"Y" AS A VOWEL
HOME KEYS AND TOP ROW

WHAT TO DO: Use TWO spaces after the two letter blends, but only ONE space after the three letter words.

WARM UP: ("YY" SPACE SPACE)

yy yy yy yy yy yy yy yy yy yy yy yy yy yy yy yy

yy yy yy yy yy yy yy yy yy yy yy yy yy yy yy yy

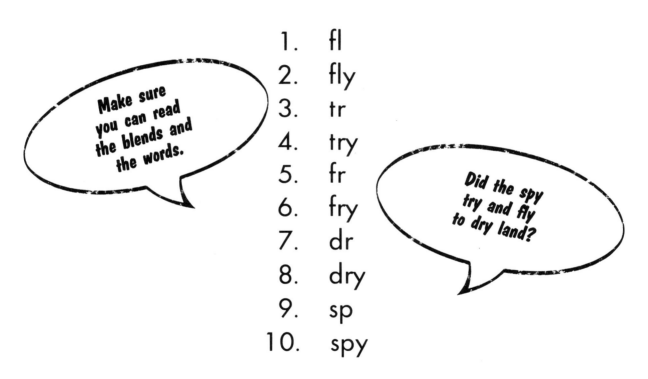

Make sure you can read the blends and the words.

Did the spy try and fly to dry land?

1. fl
2. fly
3. tr
4. try
5. fr
6. fry
7. dr
8. dry
9. sp
10. spy

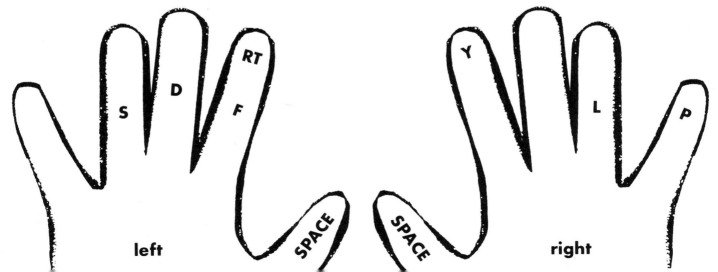

left   SPACE   SPACE   right

27

TOP ROW
HAND COORDINATION EXERCISE
"Both hands together!"

WHAT TO DO: Type each exercise for TWO lines, with TWO spaces between the letters.

SAMPLES: (QQ space space PP space space)

qq pp qq pp qq pp qq pp qq pp qq pp qq pp
qq pp qq pp qq pp qq pp qq pp qq pp qq pp

1. QQ PP ——little fingers
2. WW OO ——4th fingers
3. EE II ——3rd fingers
4. RR UU ⎫
5. TT YY ⎭ Index fingers

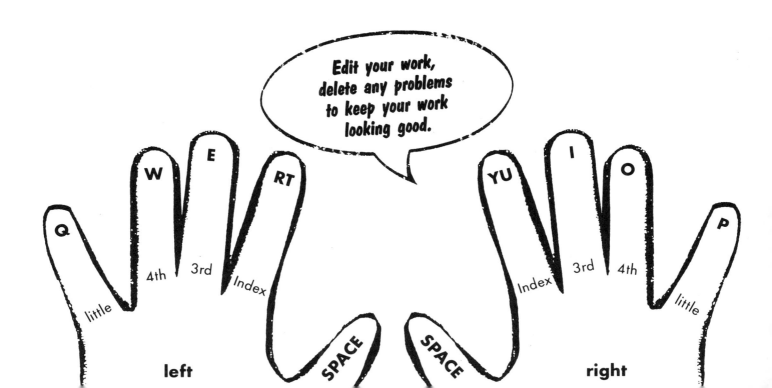

FILL IN
THE VOWELS
A, E, I, O, U

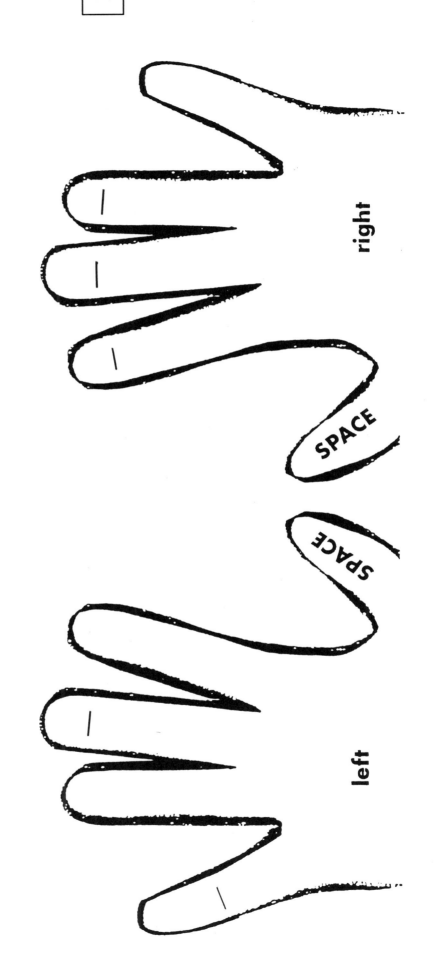

right

left

SPACE

SPACE

VOWEL PRACTICE - "A"
THE "AG" GROUP

WHAT TO DO: Check the fingering. Do the 4 beat Warm Up, then type each word for two lines, with the normal one space between each word.

WARM UP: ("AG" SPACE SPACE)

ag ag ag ag ag ag ag ag ag ag ag ag ag ag
ag ag ag ag ag ag ag ag ag ag ag ag ag ag

1. rag
2. tag
3. wag
4. lag
5. hag
6. jag
7. gag
8. sag
9. flag
10. drag

Edit out any problems to keep your work accurate.

Gag the hag with the flag, then drag her to the jag.

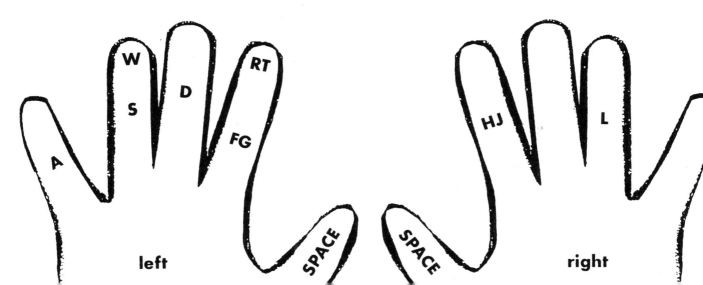

left   right

30

VOWEL PRACTICE - "E"
THE "ET" GROUP

WHAT TO DO: Read and then type the words. Use one space between them, apart from the 4-beat Warm Up where you use two spaces. Edit your errors.

WARM UP: ("ET" SPACE SPACE)

4-beat drill.

et et et et et et et et et et et et et et et et et

et et et et et et et et et et et et et et et et

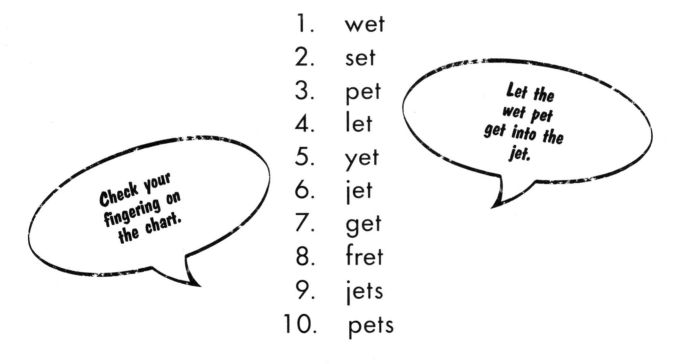

1. wet
2. set
3. pet
4. let
5. yet
6. jet
7. get
8. fret
9. jets
10. pets

Check your fingering on the chart.

Let the wet pet get into the jet.

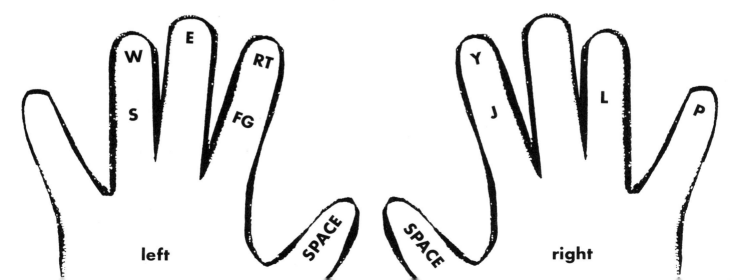

left   right

31

VOWEL PRACTICE - "I"
THE "IT" GROUP

WHAT TO DO: Read the words and do the warm up exercise. Then type the words putting one space between them. Try and edit out any problems.

4-beat drill.

WARM UP: ("IT" SPACE SPACE)

it it it it it it it it it it it it it it it it it it it it it it it
it it it it it it it it it it it it it it it it it it it it it it it

1. wit
2. sit
3. pit
4. fit
5. hit
6. lit
7. slit
8. spit
9. grit
10. quit

Quit spitting!

One space between the words.

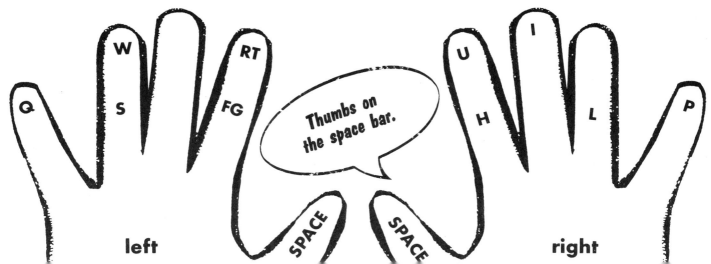

Thumbs on the space bar.

left   right

VOWEL PRACTICE - "O"
THE "OT" GROUP

WHAT TO DO: Read the words and do the 4 beat warm up. Then type each word as many times as you can for TWO lines. Delete out any mistakes.

WARM UP: ("OT" SPACE SPACE)

ot ot ot ot ot ot ot ot ot ot ot ot ot ot ot ot
ot ot ot ot ot ot ot ot ot ot ot ot ot ot ot ot

1. hot
2. pot
3. rot
4. lot
5. jot
6. got
7. dot
8. trot
9. plot
10. shot

4-beat drill.

I've got a lot of hot food in this pot.

Use the chart to check your fingering.

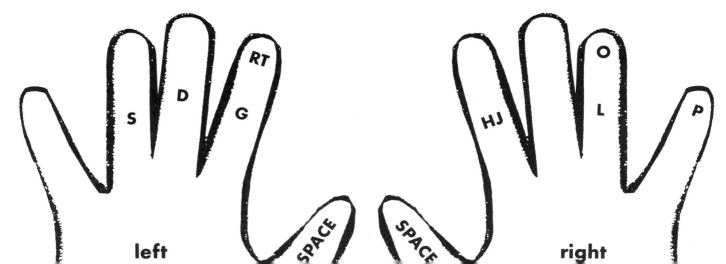

left   right

33

VOWEL PRACTICE - "U"
THE "UG" GROUP

WHAT TO DO: Read the "ug" family words. Do the rhythmic warm up and then type the words. Try and get rid of any errors with your DELETE keys.

WARM UP: ("UG" SPACE SPACE)

ug ug ug ug ug ug ug ug ug ug ug ug ug ug
ug ug ug ug ug ug ug ug ug ug ug ug ug ug

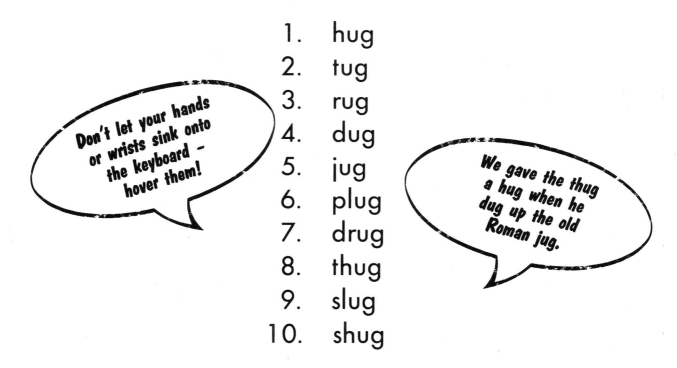

1. hug
2. tug
3. rug
4. dug
5. jug
6. plug
7. drug
8. thug
9. slug
10. shug

Don't let your hands or wrists sink onto the keyboard – hover them!

We gave the thug a hug when he dug up the old Roman jug.

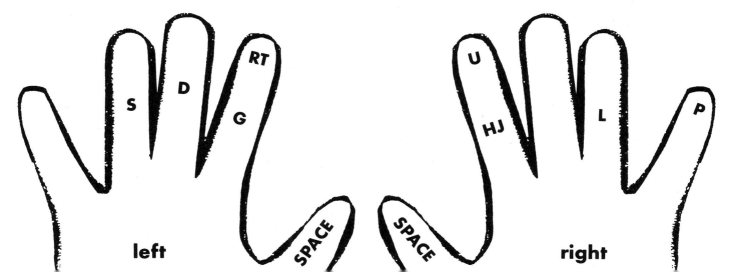

left   right

34

CLOSED SYLLABLES
HOME KEYS AND TOP ROWS

WHAT TO DO: There are 25 closed syllables on the sheet. Type each closed syllable for ONE line. You can type them in any order. Circle them as you type them. As they are all TWO letters, use TWO spaces to get a good 4 beat drill. OR if you prefer, lay out the syllables exactly as below, using the TAB key to space them out and keep them in columns.

SAMPLE: at at at at at at at at at at at

at	ap	ad	ag	as
et	ep	ed	eg	es
it	ip	id	ig	is
ot	op	od	og	os
ut	up	ud	ug	us

35

HOME KEYS AND TOP ROW
THE "EE" GROUP

WHAT TO DO: Read the words. Do the 4 beat warm up drill and then type the words. Edit out any problems you get.

WARM UP: ("EE" SPACE SPACE)

ee ee ee ee ee ee ee ee ee ee ee ee ee ee ee
ee ee ee ee ee ee ee ee ee ee ee ee ee ee ee

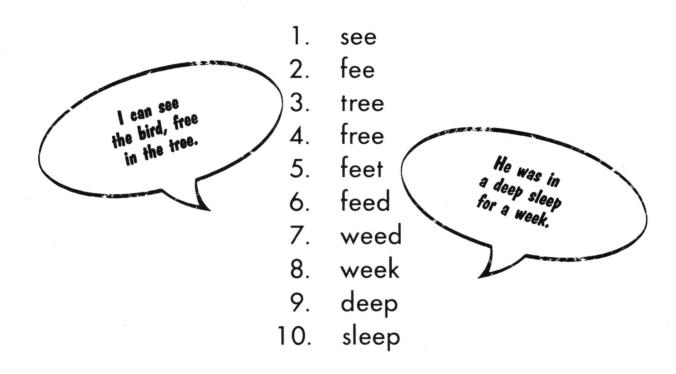

1. see
2. fee
3. tree
4. free
5. feet
6. feed
7. weed
8. week
9. deep
10. sleep

I can see the bird, free in the tree.

He was in a deep sleep for a week.

Hover your hands.

left   right

FILL IN THE TOP ROW

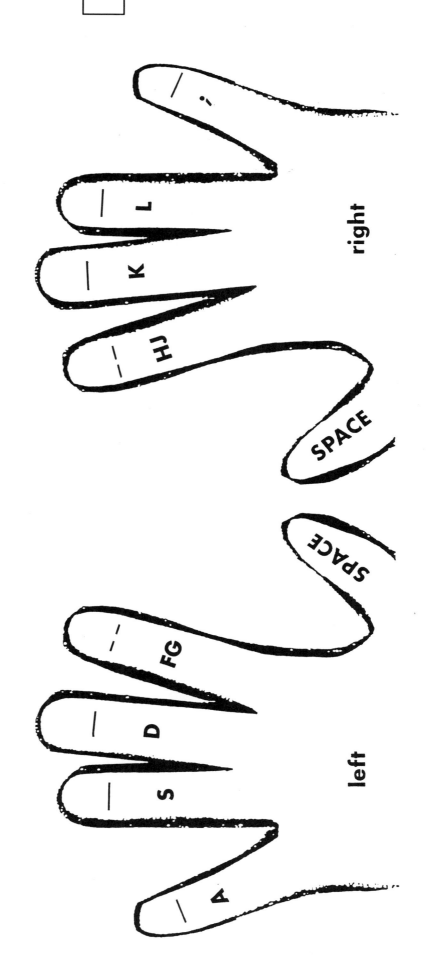

37

HIGH FREQUENCY WORDS - TWO LETTERS
HOME KEYS AND TOP ROWS

WHAT TO DO: These useful words have no pattern, so check the fingering carefully before typing each one. TWO letters, TWO spaces, TWO lines.

SAMPLE: ("TO" SPACE SPACE)

to to to to to to to to to to to to to to to to to
to to to to to to to to to to to to to to to to to

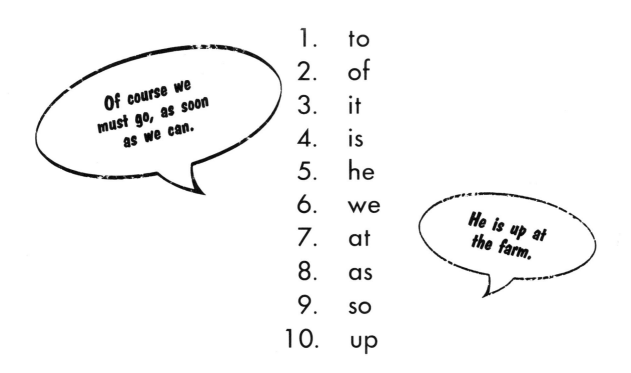

1. to
2. of
3. it
4. is
5. he
6. we
7. at
8. as
9. so
10. up

Of course we must go, as soon as we can.

He is up at the farm.

Thumbs on the space bar.

left   right

38

HIGH FREQUENCY WORDS – THREE LETTERS
HOME KEYS AND TOP ROWS

WHAT TO DO: These common words have no pattern. Check your finger chart carefully before you type each word. THREE letters, TWO lines, ONE space.

SAMPLE: ("THE" SPACE)

the the the the the the the the the the the the the
the the the the the the the the the the the the the

1. the
2. was
3. you
4. for
5. are
6. had
7. all
8. she
9. his
10. out

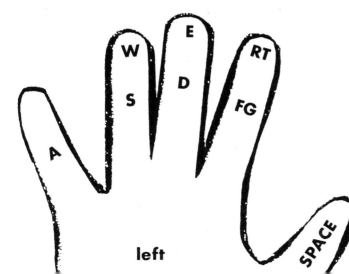

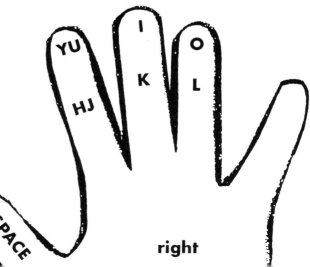

left   right

39

HIGH FREQUENCY WORDS - FOUR LETTERS
HOME KEYS AND TOP ROW

WHAT TO DO: There is no pattern to these much used words, so check out the fingering carefully on the chart. ONE space between the words.

Edit your work to keep it looking good!

SAMPLE: ("THAT" SPACE)

that that that that that that that that that that that
that that that that that that that that that that that

1. that
2. they
3. with
4. this
5. were
6. will
7. said
8. what
9. your
10. year

We were going on holiday with your friends this year.

What will they say to your mother?

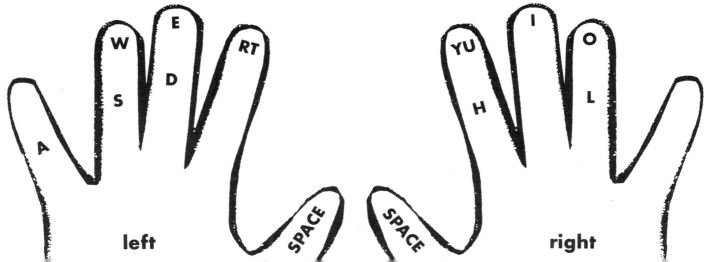

left   right

40

HOME AND TOP ROWS
WORK WITH "THE"

WHAT TO DO: Either type the words as many times as you can for ONE line as in the sample.

Sample: the fly the fly the fly the fly the fly the fly

OR: lay the Exercise out exactly as below, making sure that the numbers and words line up.

Warm up: the   the   the   the   the   the   the
                the   the   the   the   the   the   the

1. the fly
2. the spy
3. the rag
4. the hag
5. the jet
6. the pet
7. the jug
8. the thug
9. the tree
10. the week

Edit your work. Make the mistakes invisible.

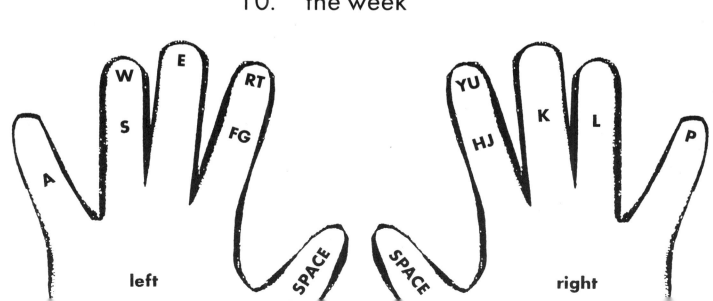

41

PHRASE BUILDING
HOME AND TOP ROWS

WHAT TO DO: Either type each phrase as many times as you can for ONE line as in the sample.

SAMPLE: at the at the at the at the at the at the

OR: Lay out the work exactly as on this page, keeping the numbers and words lined up.

1. at the
2. at the feet
3. up the
4. up the tree
5. all the
6. all the years
7. for the
8. for the pets
9. out of
10. out of gas

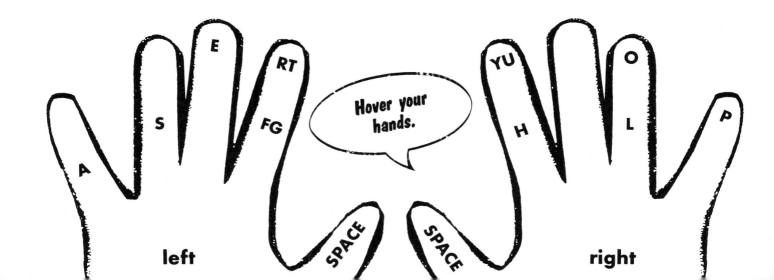

42

SENTENCE BUILDING

WHAT TO DO: Copy the sentence triangles below. Edit your work to get each triangle right once. Remember the capital letters and full stops.

A. The
The fly
The fly is
The fly is dry.

B. The
The pet
The pet is
The pet is wet.

C. The
The pot
The pot is
The pot is hot.

D. The
The pit
The pit is
The pit is lit.

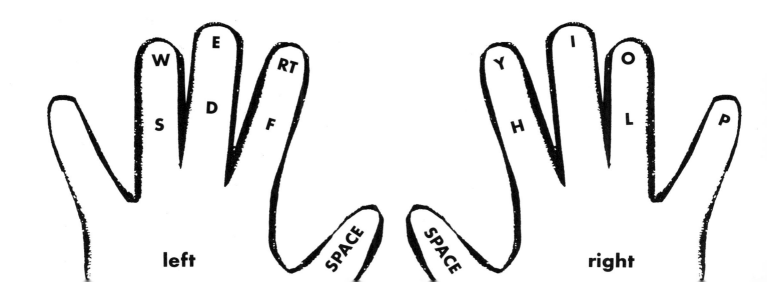

left   right

43

MAKING SHAPES
TOP ROW DIAMOND

WHAT TO DO: Check the Top Row fingering. Copy the Diamond Shape below using your CENTRING FUNCTION to get each line in the right position. Notice that the middle line is in BOLD PRINT so you will need to find out how to get BOLD on your word processor. The number of times you need to type each letter is written down the right hand side of the paper to help you. There are TWO spaces between the letters. An equidistant font (see Teacher's Notes Font Choice) works best for this diamond shape.

```
                        QQ                                  QQ  x   1
                     PP    PP                               PP  x   2
                  WW    WW    WW                            WW  x   3
               OO    OO    OO    OO                         OO  x   4
            EE    EE    EE    EE    EE                      EE  x   5
         II    II    II    II    II    II                   II  x   6
      RR    RR    RR    RR    RR    RR    RR                RR  x   7
   UU    UU    UU    UU    UU    UU    UU    UU             UU  x   8
TT    TT    TT    TT    TT    TT    TT    TT    TT          TT  x   9
YY  YY  YY  YY  YY  YY  YY  YY  YY  YY                      YY  x  10
TT    TT    TT    TT    TT    TT    TT    TT    TT          TT  x   9
   UU    UU    UU    UU    UU    UU    UU    UU             UU  x   8
      RR    RR    RR    RR    RR    RR    RR                RR  x   7
         II    II    II    II    II    II                   II  x   6
            EE    EE    EE    EE    EE                      EE  x   5
               OO    OO    OO    OO                         OO  x   4
                  WW    WW    WW                            WW  x   3
                     PP    PP                               PP  x   2
                        QQ                                  QQ  x   1
```

MAKING SHAPES
TOP ROW LADDER AND FLAG

WHAT TO DO: Copy the ladder below, which is made from the Top Row letters. Use TABS to position the uprights of the ladder. An equidistant font (see Teacher's Notes) works best for the ladder.

Find out how to set tabs and use the tab key for the ladder.

```
II              II
II              II
IIQQQQQQQQQQQQII
II              II
IIPPPPPPPPPPPPII
II              II
IIWWWWWWWWWWWWII
II              II
IIOOOOOOOOOOOOII
II              II
IIEEEEEEEEEEEEII
II              II
IIRRRRRRRRRRRRII
II              II
IITTTTTTTTTTTTII
II              II
IIUUUUUUUUUUUUII
II              II
IIYYYYYYYYYYYYII
II              II
II              II
```

WHAT TO DO: Copy the flag below which is made from the Top Row letters. Use the TAB key to position the flag pole. An equidistant font works well for the flag.

```
IIQQQQQQQQQQQQQQQQQQQQQQQQQ
IIIPPPPPPPPPPPPPPPPPPPPPPP
IIWWWWWWWWWWWWWWWWWWWW
IIIOOOOOOOOOOOOOOOOOO
IIIEEEEEEEEEEEEEEEE
IIIUUUUUUUUUUUUUUUUUU
IIRRRRRRRRRRRRRRRRRRR
IIIYYYYYYYYYYYYYYYYYYYY
IIITTTTTTTTTTTTTTTTTTTTTTTT
III
III
III
III
III
III
III
```

You can change the design if you want – but use top row letters.

Part Three

BOTTOM ROW MODULE

CONTENTS

Use the Contents Page as a Record Sheet. Tick off the pages you have done in the boxes on the right.

PART THREE – BOTTOM ROW MODULE   Page

BOTTOM ROW

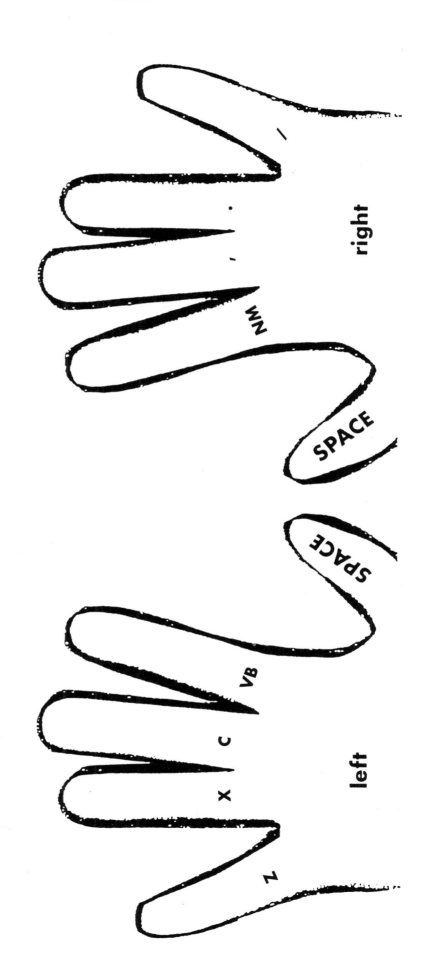

BOTTOM ROW
Fill in the
Home Keys

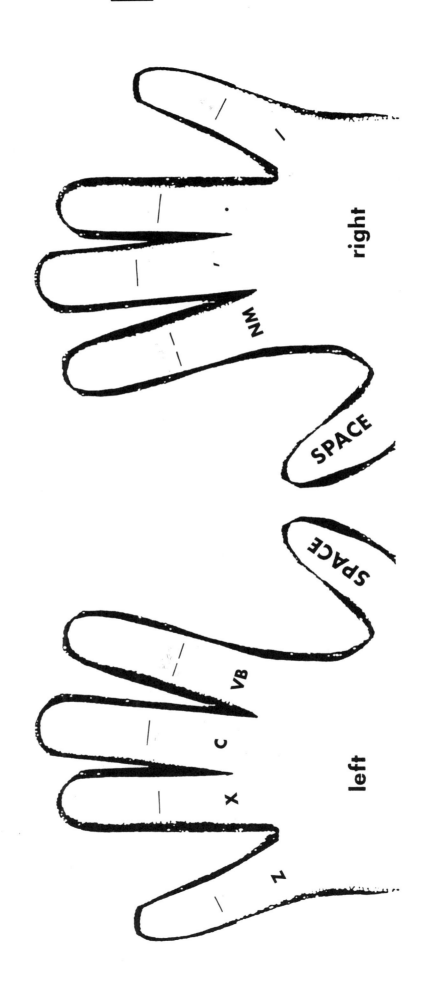

right

left

NM

SPACE

SPACE

VB

C

X

Z

LEARN THE BOTTOM ROW
TEN NEW LETTERS!

WHAT TO DO: Look at your chart and see how your fingers fit onto the bottom row. Get used to moving your fingers up and down the keyboard. Type each letter with two spaces for two rows.

SAMPLE: ("ZZ" SPACE SPACE)

ZZ ZZ ZZ ZZ ZZ ZZ ZZ ZZ ZZ ZZ ZZ ZZ ZZ ZZ ZZ
ZZ ZZ ZZ ZZ ZZ ZZ ZZ ZZ ZZ ZZ ZZ ZZ ZZ ZZ ZZ

1. ZZ
2. //
3. XX
4. ..
5. CC
6. ,,
7. VV
8. MM
9. BB
10. NN

Try and keep a strong 4-beat rhythm.

Now you know 30 keys.

Look out for the full stop and comma.

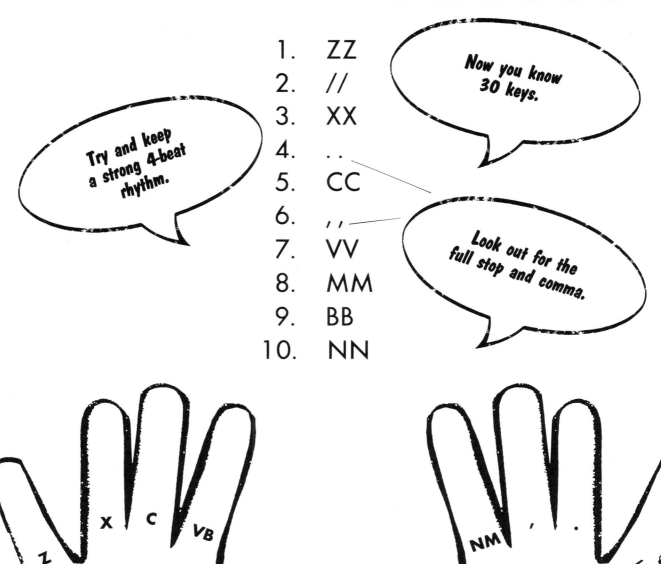

48

HOME AND BOTTOM ROWS
"HOME TO BASE"

WHAT TO DO: Make sure the same finger types the two letters in the drill. Type ALL THE TWOs - TWO letters, TWO spaces, TWO lines as in the sample.

SAMPLE: ("AZ" SPACE SPACE)

az az az az az az az az az az az az az az

az az az az az az az az az az az az az az

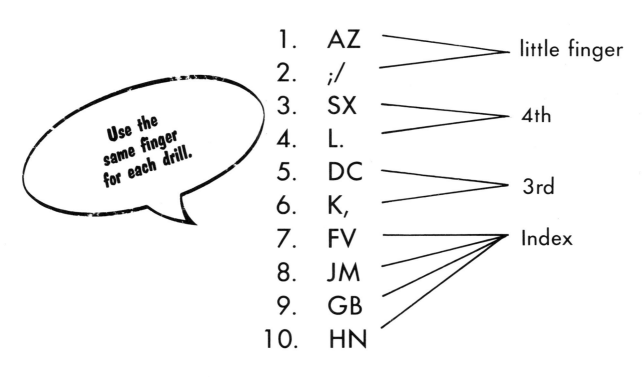

Use the same finger for each drill.

1. AZ ——————⟩ little finger
2. ;/
3. SX ——————⟩ 4th
4. L.
5. DC ——————⟩ 3rd
6. K,
7. FV ——————⟩ Index
8. JM
9. GB
10. HN

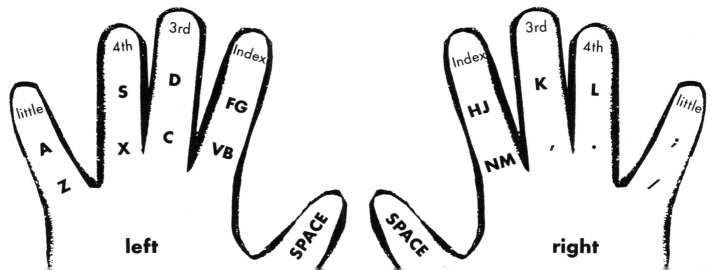

left   right

49

BOTTOM, HOME AND TOP ROWS
"ALL THE WAY UP!"

WHAT TO DO: Make sure the SAME finger types the letters in each drill. Use ONE space only to keep the strong 4 beat rhythm, as in the sample.

SAMPLE: ("ZAQ" SPACE)

zaq zaq zaq zaq zaq zaq zaq zaq zaq zaq zaq
zaq zaq zaq zaq zaq zaq zaq zaq zaq zaq zaq

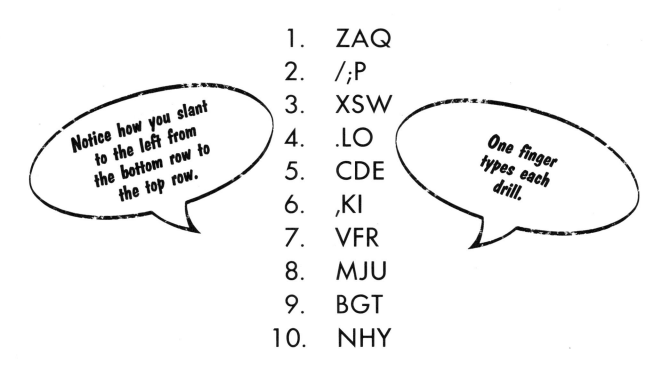

1. ZAQ
2. /;P
3. XSW
4. .LO
5. CDE
6. ,KI
7. VFR
8. MJU
9. BGT
10. NHY

Notice how you slant to the left from the bottom row to the top row.

One finger types each drill.

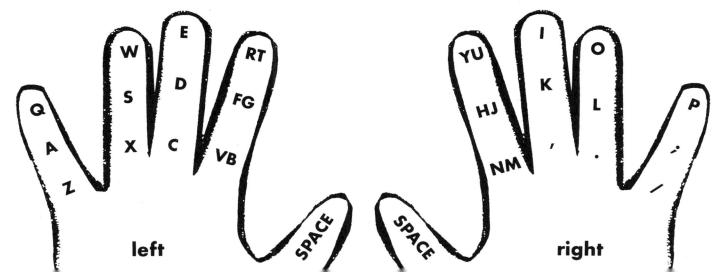

left   right

50

OPEN SYLLABLES
ALL THREE LETTER ROWS

WHAT TO DO: There are 25 open syllables below, Type each closed syllable for ONE line. You can type them in any order. Circle them when you have typed them. As they are all TWO letters, use TWO spaces to get a good 4 beat drill. OR if you prefer, lay out the syllables exactly as below, using the TAB key to space them out and keep them in columns.

SAMPLE: na na na na na na na na na na na na

---

na	ne	ni	no	nu
pa	pe	pi	po	pu
ba	be	bi	bo	bu
ca	ce	ci	co	cu
va	ve	vi	vo	vu

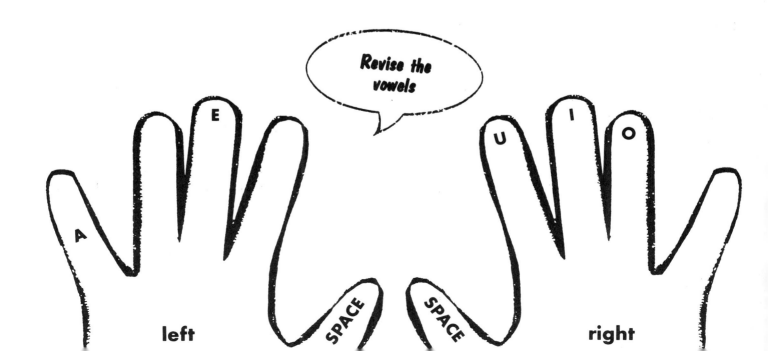

Revise the vowels

left   right

51

CONSONANT BLENDS
ALL THREE LETTER ROWS

WHAT TO DO: Read the blends. Check your fingering on the chart and then type - TWO letters, TWO spaces, TWO lines. Edit out any problems.

SAMPLE: ("CR" SPACE SPACE)

cr cr cr cr cr cr cr cr cr cr cr cr cr cr cr cr cr cr

cr cr cr cr cr cr cr cr cr cr cr cr cr cr cr cr cr cr

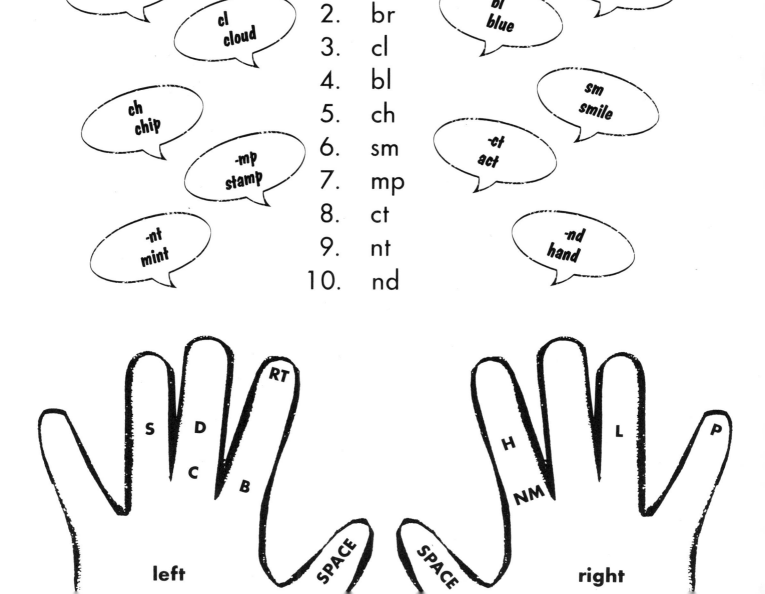

cr crab
cl cloud
ch chip
-mp stamp
-nt mint
br brown
bl blue
sm smile
-ct act
-nd hand

1. cr
2. br
3. cl
4. bl
5. ch
6. sm
7. mp
8. ct
9. nt
10. nd

S D RT C B

H L P NM

SPACE SPACE

left   right

52

VOWEL PRACTICE
WORK ON 'A'
THE "AM" GROUP

WHAT TO DO: Read the words then type each one as many times as you can for two rows. One space between the words apart from the warm up.

4-beat drill.

WARM UP: ("AM" SPACE SPACE)

am am am am am am am am am am am am

am am am am am am am am am am am am

1.   ram
2.   dam
3.   ham
4.   jam
5.   Sam
6.   Pam
7.   tram
8.   spam
9.   pram
10. slam

Sam and Pam are harder to type. One line is O.K.

Hold down the right hand shift key while you type the capital S for Sam.

Hold down the left hand shift key while you type capital P for Pam.

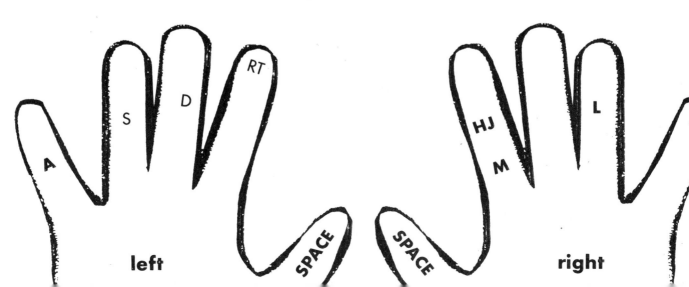

left   right

53

VOWEL PRACTICE
WORK ON E"
THE "EN" GROUP

WHAT TO DO: Read and then type the words for two rows each. Use one space between each word apart from the Warm Up.

WARM UP: ("EN" SPACE SPACE)

en en en en en en en en en en en en en en en

en en en en en en en en en en en en en en en

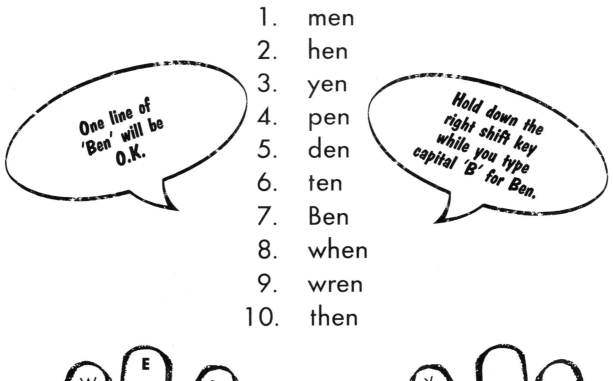

1. men
2. hen
3. yen
4. pen
5. den
6. ten
7. Ben
8. when
9. wren
10. then

One line of 'Ben' will be O.K.

Hold down the right shift key while you type capital 'B' for Ben.

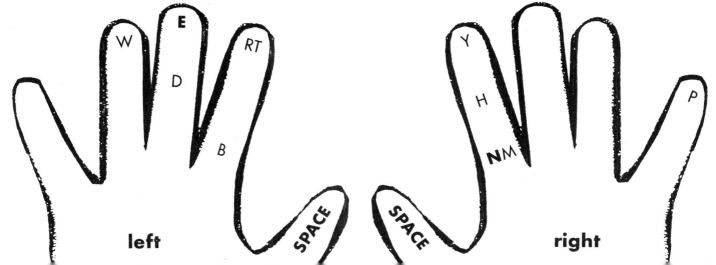

left   SPACE   SPACE   **right**

54

SENTENCE BUILDING
VOWEL PRACTICE
"A" AND "E"

WHAT TO DO: Copy the sentence triangles below. Try and get each triangle right once. Remember the CAPITAL letters and full stops.

Practise the "A"

A
A man
A man sat
A man sat an
A man sat an exam.

Hold down the right shift key and type the capital 'A'.

Practise the "E"

There
There were
There were ten
There were ten hens.

Hold down the right shift key and type the capital 'T'.

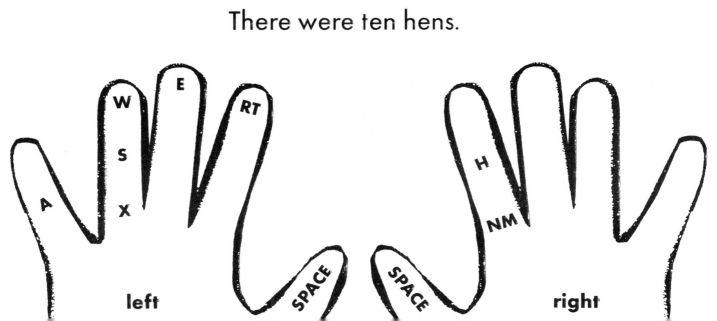

left   SPACE   SPACE   right

55

VOWEL PRACTICE
WORK ON "I"
THE "IN" GROUP

WHAT TO DO: Read and then type the words for two rows. Once space between the words, but TWO spaces for the Warm Up.

WARM UP: ("IN" SPACE SPACE)

4 beats

in in in in in in in in in in in in in in in in in in

in in in in in in in in in in in in in in in in in in

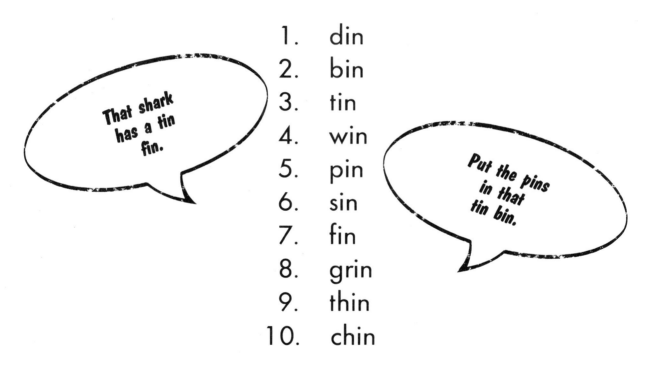

That shark has a tin fin.

1. din
2. bin
3. tin
4. win
5. pin
6. sin
7. fin
8. grin
9. thin
10. chin

Put the pins in that tin bin.

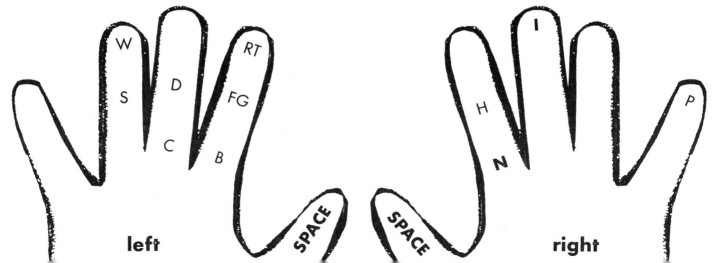

left   SPACE   SPACE   right

56

VOWEL PRACTICE
WORK ON "O"
THE "OB" GROUP

WHAT TO DO: Read and then type the words for two lines. Use one space between the words, but two spaces in the Warm Up.

WARM UP: ("OB" SPACE SPACE)

ob ob ob ob ob ob ob ob ob ob ob ob ob ob
ob ob ob ob ob ob ob ob ob ob ob ob ob ob

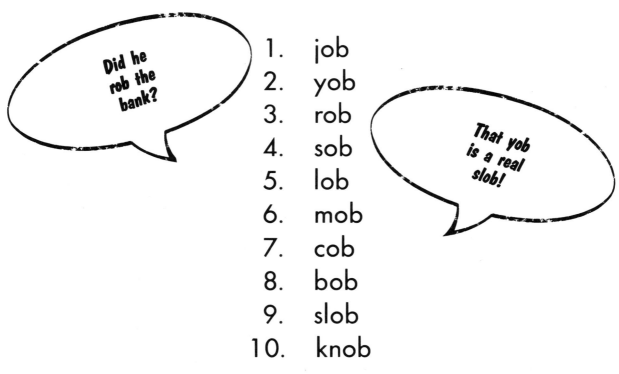

1. job
2. yob
3. rob
4. sob
5. lob
6. mob
7. cob
8. bob
9. slob
10. knob

Did he rob the bank?

That yob is a real slob!

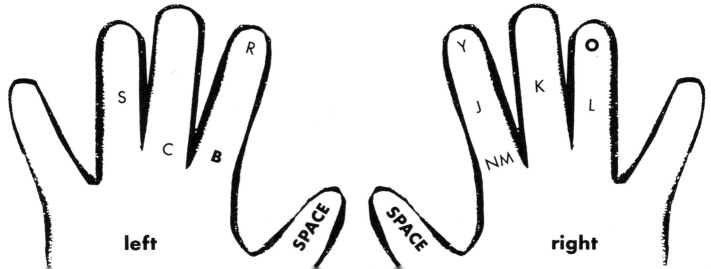

left   SPACE   SPACE   right

57

PHRASE BUILDING
USING "IN" AND "ON"

WHAT TO DO: Either type each phrase as many times as you can for ONE line as in the sample.

SAMPLE: in the bin in the bin in the bin in the bin

OR: copy the exercise exactly as below, lining up the numbers and words.

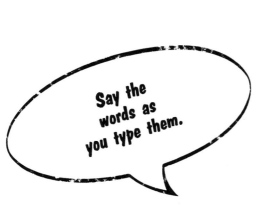

Say the words as you type them.

1.　in the bin
2.　in the sin bin
3.　in the tin
4.　in the pin tin

5.　on the chin
6.　on the thin chin
7.　on the fin
8.　on the thin fin

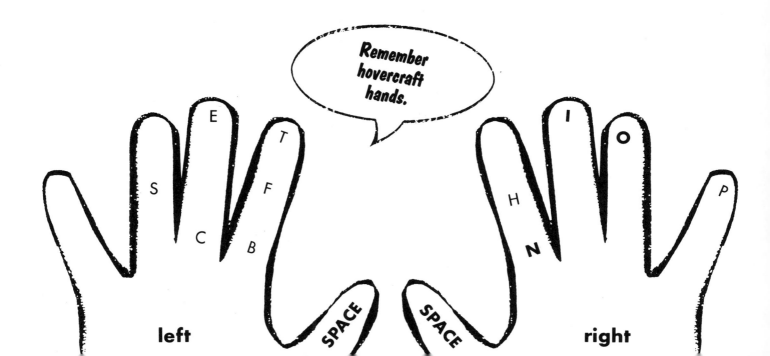

Remember hovercraft hands.

left　　SPACE　SPACE　　right

58

VOWEL PRACTICE
WORK ON "U"
THE "UB" GROUP

WHAT TO DO: Type each word for two lines. One space between words, two spaces for the Warm Up drill.

WARM UP: ("UB" SPACE SPACE)

ub ub ub ub ub ub ub ub ub ub ub ub ub ub
ub ub ub ub ub ub ub ub ub ub ub ub ub ub

1. rub
2. tub
3. sub
4. dub
5. cub
6. club
7. grub
8. snub
9. stub
10. shrub

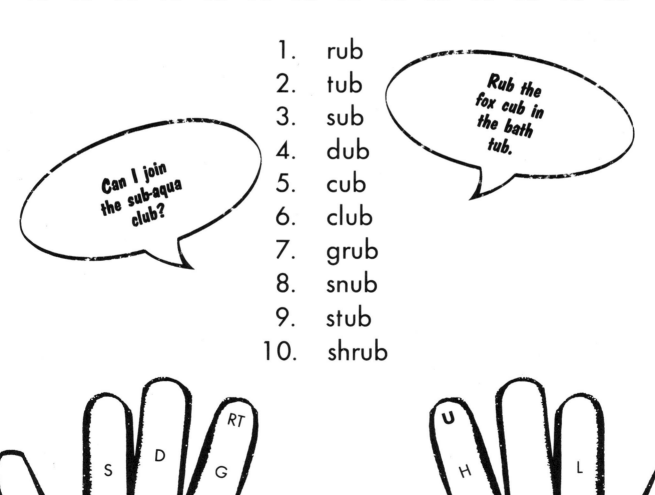

Can I join the sub-aqua club?

Rub the fox cub in the bath tub.

left

SPACE SPACE

right

SENTENCE BUILDING
VOWEL PRACTICE – "I", "O" AND "U"

WHAT TO DO: Copy the sentence triangles as they are below.

Practise the "i"

Did
Did it
Did it win?

Practise the "o"

Our
Our shop
Our shop is
Our shop is open.

Practise the "u"

Our
Our club
Our club is
Our club is shut.

THREE LETTER BLENDS

WHAT TO DO: Type each blend for TWO rows with ONE space between the rows.

SAMPLE: str str str str str str str str str str str str str str
str str str str str str str str str str str str str str

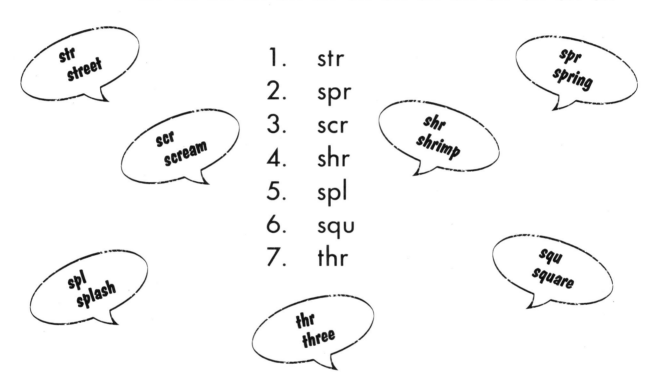

1. str
2. spr
3. scr
4. shr
5. spl
6. squ
7. thr

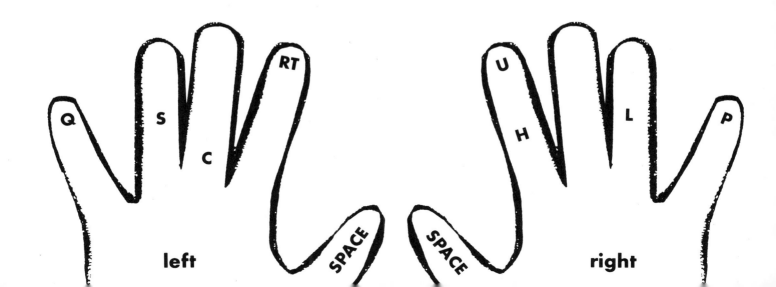

left   right

FILL IN THE BOTTOM ROW

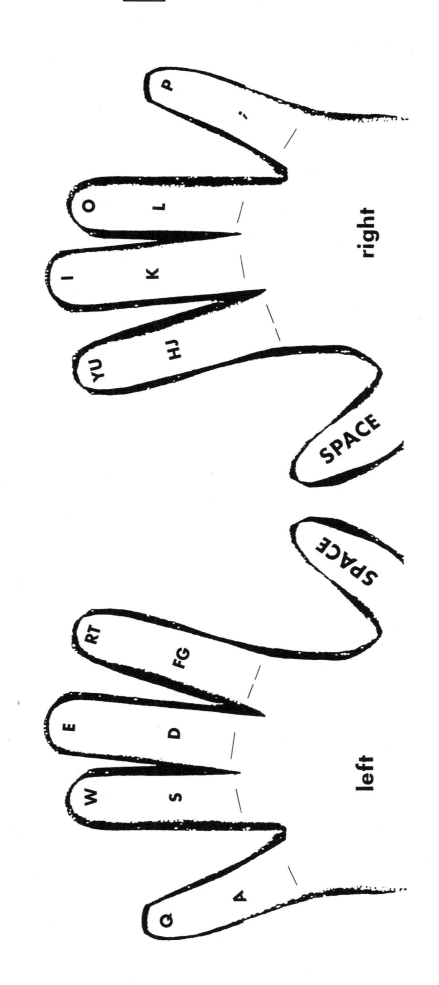

MAKING SHAPES
BOTTOM ROW TRIANGLES

WHAT TO DO: Check your bottom row fingering. Copy the triangles below, using the CENTRING FUNCTION on the word processor to make the shape The number of each letter pair your need is written down the right hand side of the page. Choose an equidistant font (see Teacher's Notes Font Choice) for this exercise.

LOWER CASE BOTTOM ROW TRIANGLE

```
                    zz                          zz  x  1
              //    //                          //  x  2
           xx    xx    xx                       xx  x  3
          ..   ..   ..   ..                     ..  x  4
        cc   cc   cc   cc   cc                   cc  x  5
        ''  ''  ''  ''  ''  ''                   ,,  x  6
      vv  vv  vv  vv  vv  vv  vv                 vv  x  7
    mm  mm  mm  mm  mm  mm  mm  mm                mm  x  8
  bb  bb  bb  bb  bb  bb  bb  bb  bb              bb  x  9
nn  nn  nn  nn  nn  nn  nn  nn  nn  nn            nn  x 10
```

Get good at centring.

UPPER CASE BOTTOM ROW TRIANGLE

```
                    ZZ                          ZZ  x  1
              //    //                          //  x  2
           XX    XX    XX                       XX  x  3
          ..   ..   ..   ..                     ..  x  4
        CC   CC   CC   CC   CC                   CC  x  5
        ''  ''  ''  ''  ''  ''                   ,,  x  6
      VV  VV  VV  VV  VV  VV  VV                 VV  x  7
    MM  MM  MM  MM  MM  MM  MM  MM                MM  x  8
  BB  BB  BB  BB  BB  BB  BB  BB  BB              BB  x  9
NN  NN  NN  NN  NN  NN  NN  NN  NN  NN            NN  x 10
```

Lock into caps.

MAKING SHAPES
BOTTOM ROW DIAMOND

WHAT TO DO: Copy the diamond shape below, which is made from the Bottom Row letters. Use you CENTRING FUNCTION to make the shape. Notice that the middle line is in BOLD print so make sure you know how to get this on your word processor. The number of times you need to type each key is written down the right hand side of the page. Only an equidistant font (see Teacher's Notes Font Choice) will centre accurately.

```
                    ZZ                           ZZ  x  1
                  //  //                         //  x  2
                XX  XX  XX                        XX  x  3
              ..  ..  ..  ..                       ..  x  4
            CC  CC  CC  CC  CC                     CC  x  5
          ''  ''  ''  ''  ''  ''                   ,,  x  6
        VV  VV  VV  VV  VV  VV  VV                 VV  x  7
      MM  MM  MM  MM  MM  MM  MM  MM               MM  x  8
    BB  BB  BB  BB  BB  BB  BB  BB  BB             BB  x  9
  NN  NN  NN  NN  NN  NN  NN  NN  NN  NN           NN  x 10
    BB  BB  BB  BB  BB  BB  BB  BB  BB             BB  x  9
      MM  MM  MM  MM  MM  MM  MM  MM               MM  x  8
        VV  VV  VV  VV  VV  VV  VV                 VV  x  7
          ''  ''  ''  ''  ''  ''                   ,,  x  6
            CC  CC  CC  CC  CC                     CC  x  5
              ..  ..  ..  ..                       ..  x  4
                XX  XX  XX                        XX  x  3
                  //  //                          //  x  2
                    ZZ                           ZZ  x  1
```

Don't forget the bold!

MAKING SHAPES
BOTTOM ROW LADDER

WHAT TO DO: Copy the ladder below, which is made of up of bottom Row Keys. Use the TAB key to line up the uprights and try and get your ladder across the centre of the page. Use an equidistant font to make the ladder.

Get help to use the tabs.

```
          //               //
          //               //
          //...........//
          //               //
          //ZZZZZZZZZZ//
          //               //
          //XXXXXXXXXX//
          //               //
          //CCCCCCCCCC//
          //               //
          //VVVVVVVVVV//
          //               //
          //BBBBBBBBBB//
          //               //
          //NNNNNNNNNN//
          //               //
          //MMMMMMMMMM//
          //               //
          //,,,,,,,,,,//
          //               //
          //               //
```

BOTTOM ROW FLAG

WHAT TO DO: Copy the flag below which is made from the Bottom Row Keys. Use TABS to position the pole. Get the flag across the middle of the page. An equidistant font makes the best shape.

```
XXX,,,,,,,,,,,,,,,,,,,,,,,,,
XXX ZZZZZZZZZZZZZZZZZZZZZZZ
XXX CCCCCCCCCCCCCCCCCCCCC
XXX VVVVVVVVVVVVVVVVVVVVV
XXX /////////////////
XXX BBBBBBBBBBBBBBBBBBB
XXX NNNNNNNNNNNNNNNNNNNNN
XXX MMMMMMMMMMMMMMMMMMMMMMM
XXX ....................
XXX
XXX
XXX
XXX
XXX
XXX
XXX
```

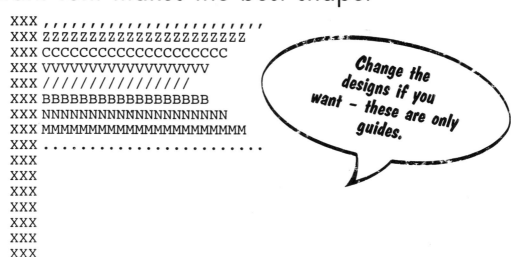

Change the designs if you want – these are only guides.

Part Four

CONSOLIDATION OR EASY START MODULE

CONTENTS

Use the Contents Page as a Record Sheet. Tick off the pages you have done in the boxes on the right.

PART FOUR – CONSOLIDATION OR EASY START MODULE

65

BASH OUT THE "B"s

INSTRUCTIONS: This sheet will help you get good at "B" and the vowels. Type the exercises below – TWO letters, TWO spaces, TWO lines.

WARM UP: (BB SPACE SPACE)

bb bb bb bb bb bb bb bb bb bb bb bb bb
bb bb bb bb bb bb bb bb bb bb bb bb bb

1. BA
2. BE
3. BI
4. BO
5. BU
6. AB
7. EB
8. IB
9. OB
10. UB

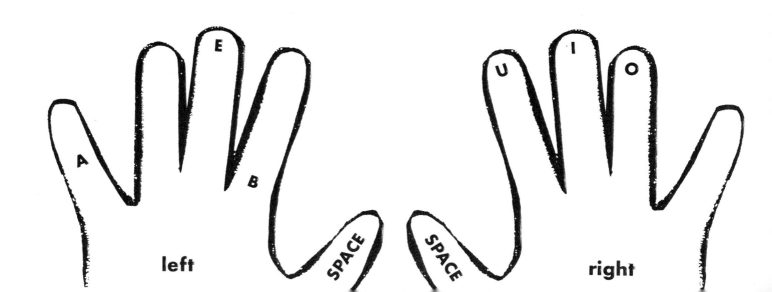

66

CONQUER THE "C"s

WHAT TO DO: This will help you learn the "C" key and practise the vowels. Type each exercise for TWO lines.

WARM UP: (CC SPACE SPACE)

cc cc cc cc cc cc cc cc cc cc cc cc cc cc cc cc

cc cc cc cc cc cc cc cc cc cc cc cc cc cc cc cc

1. CA
2. CE
3. CI
4. CO
5. CU
6. AC
7. EC
8. IC
9. OC
10. UC

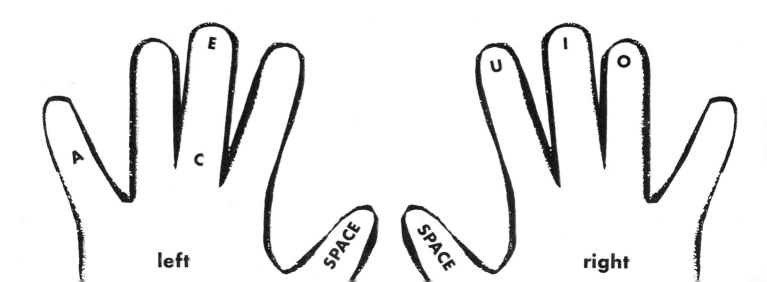

left   right

67

DEFEAT THE "D"s

WHAT TO DO: When you have done this sheet you will have defeated the "D"s and improved the vowels. Type each exercise - TWO spaces, TWO lines.

WARM UP: ("DD" SPACE SPACE)

dd dd dd dd dd dd dd dd dd dd dd dd dd dd
dd dd dd dd dd dd dd dd dd dd dd dd dd dd

1. DA
2. DE
3. DI
4. DO
5. DU
6. AD
7. ED
8. ID
9. OD
10. UD

Can you spot the proper word?

Dad did dry the daft donkey!

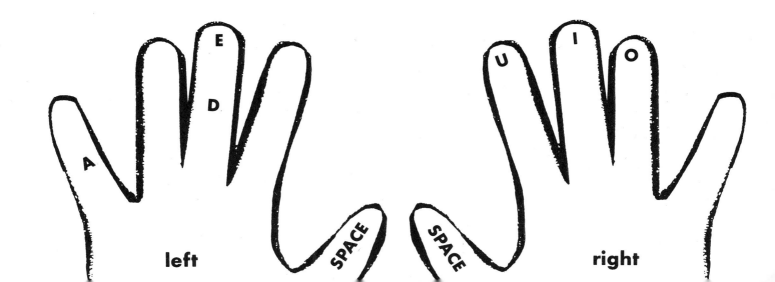

left   SPACE   SPACE   right

68

FIX THE "F"s

WHAT TO DO: By the end of this page you will have fixed the "F"s and sharpened up the vowels. TWO spaces and TWO lines for each exercise.

WARM UP: ("FF" SPACE SPACE)

ff ff ff ff ff ff ff ff ff ff ff ff ff ff ff ff ff ff ff ff
ff ff ff ff ff ff ff ff ff ff ff ff ff ff ff ff ff ff ff ff

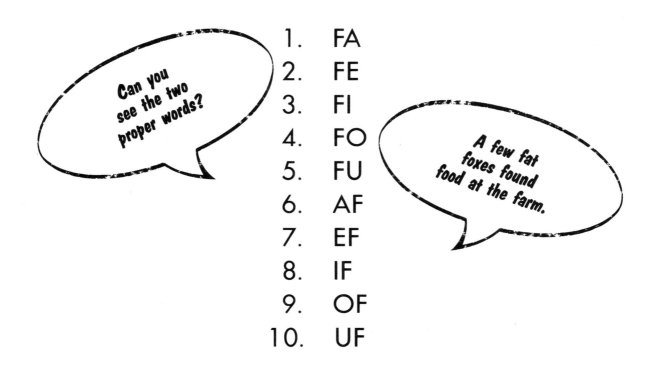

1. FA
2. FE
3. FI
4. FO
5. FU
6. AF
7. EF
8. IF
9. OF
10. UF

Can you see the two proper words?

A few fat foxes found food at the farm.

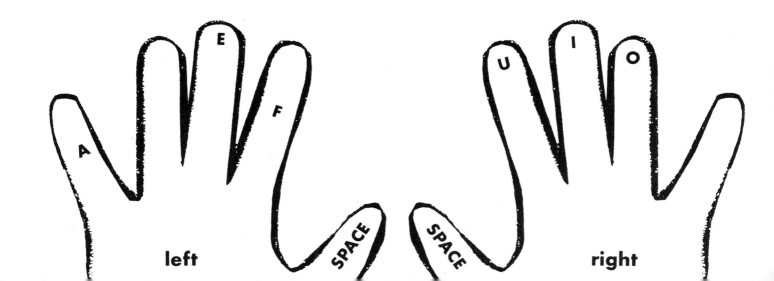

left   SPACE   SPACE   right

69

GET GOOD AT "G"

INSTRUCTIONS: This sheet will help you get good at "G" and the vowels. Type the exercises below – TWO letters, TWO spaces, TWO lines.

WARM UP: (GG SPACE SPACE)

gg gg gg gg gg gg gg gg gg gg gg gg gg gg
gg gg gg gg gg gg gg gg gg gg gg gg gg gg

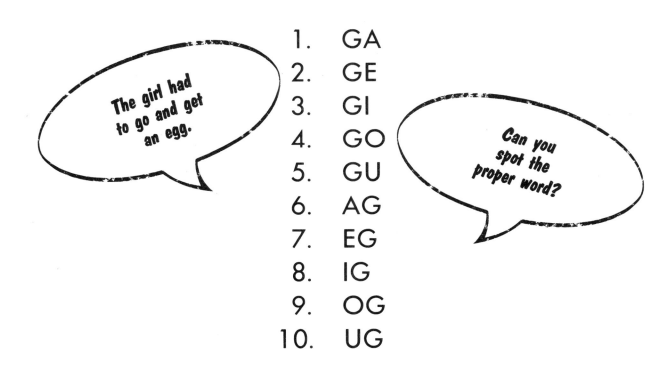

1. GA
2. GE
3. GI
4. GO
5. GU
6. AG
7. EG
8. IG
9. OG
10. UG

The girl had to go and get an egg.

Can you spot the proper word?

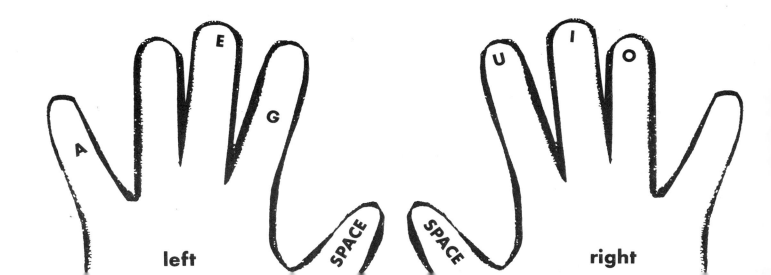

left   right

70

HAMMER OUT "H"

WHAT TO DO: Hammer out the "H" and you will never forget where it is. Type each exercise for TWO lines with TWO spaces. Try and edit out errors.

WARM UP: ("HH" SPACE SPACE)

HH HH HH HH HH HH HH HH HH HH HH HH
HH HH HH HH HH HH HH HH HH HH HH HH

1. HA
2. HE
3. HI
4. HO
5. HU
6. AH
7. EH
8. IH
9. OH
10. UH

Can you find a proper word?

He has a huge hedgehog in his house.

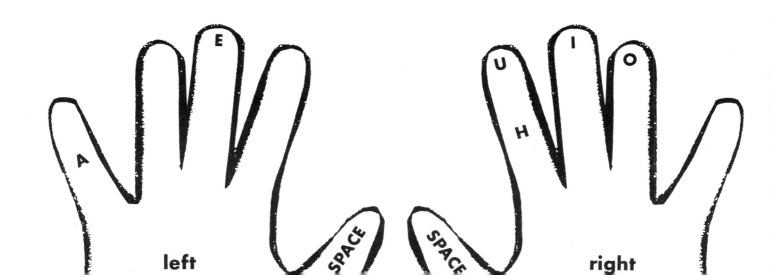

left

right

77

JET THROUGH THE J's

WHAT TO DO: Jet through this page and get good at "J" and the vowels as well. Type each drill - TWO lines, TWO spaces. Edit out any problems.

WARM UP: ("JJ" SPACE SPACE)

ii ii ii ii ii ii ii ii ii ii ii ii ii ii ii ii ii ii ii ii ii ii ii ii
ii ii ii ii ii ii ii ii ii ii ii ii ii ii ii ii ii ii ii ii ii ii ii ii

1. JA
2. JE
3. JI
4. JO
5. JU
6. AJ
7. EJ
8. IJ
9. OJ
10. UJ

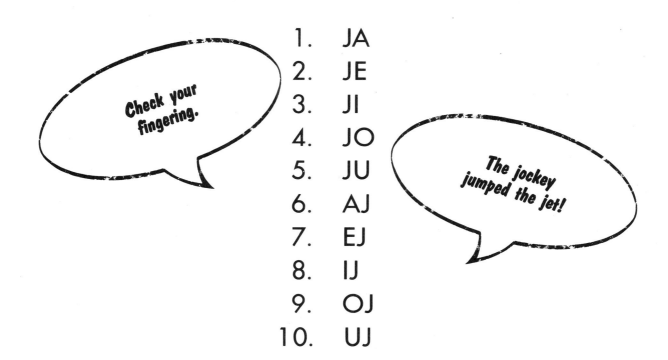

Check your fingering.

The jockey jumped the jet!

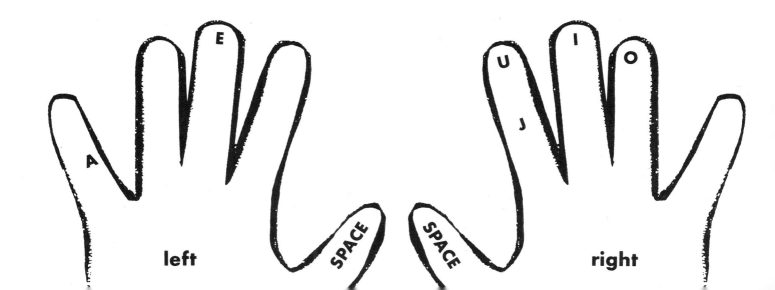

left   SPACE   SPACE   right

72

OK THE K'S

WHAT TO DO: This page will help you get OK with "K" and the vowels as well. Type each drill - TWO lines, TWO spaces and edit out any problems.

WARM UP: ("KK" SPACE SPACE)

kk kk kk kk kk kk kk kk kk kk kk kk kk kk kk
kk kk kk kk kk kk kk kk kk kk kk kk kk kk kk

1. KA
2. KE
3. KI
4. KO
5. KU
6. AK
7. EK
8. IK
9. OK
10. UK

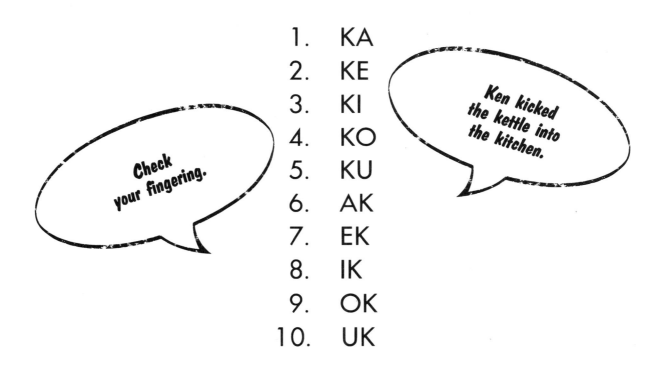

Check your fingering.

Ken kicked the kettle into the kitchen.

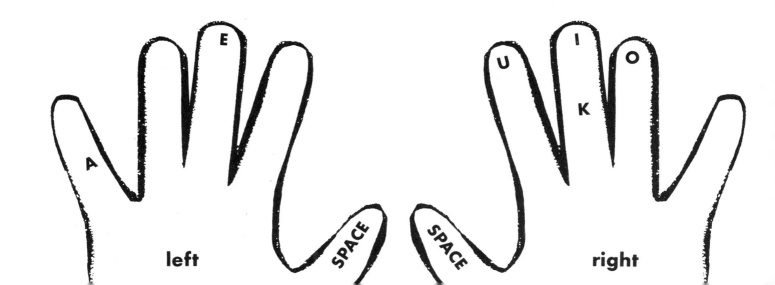

left   right

73

LOADS OF "L"

WHAT TO DO: This page gives you loads of practise with "L". Type each exercise - TWO spaces, TWO lines. Be careful not to muddle up the small "l" with the capital "I".

WARM UP: ("LL" SPACE SPACE)

ll ll ll ll ll lll ll ll ll ll ll ll ll ll ll ll ll ll ll
ll ll ll ll ll ll ll ll ll ll ll ll ll ll ll ll ll ll ll

Edit your work and get rid of any errors.

1. LA
2. LE
3. LI
4. LO
5. LU
6. AL
7. EL
8. IL
9. OL
10. UL

Lyn led the lamb up the leafy lane.

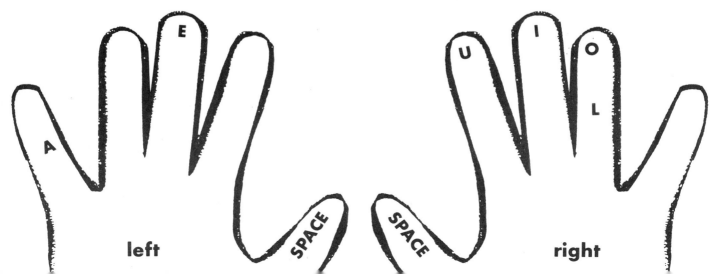

left   right

74

MASSES OF M's

WHAT TO DO: You will type masses of M's on this page and work on the vowels as well. Type each drill - TWO lines, TWO spaces, Edit your work.

WARM UP: ("MM" SPACE SPACE)

mm mm mm mm mm mm mm mm mm mm mm

mm mm mm mm mm mm mm mm mm mm mm

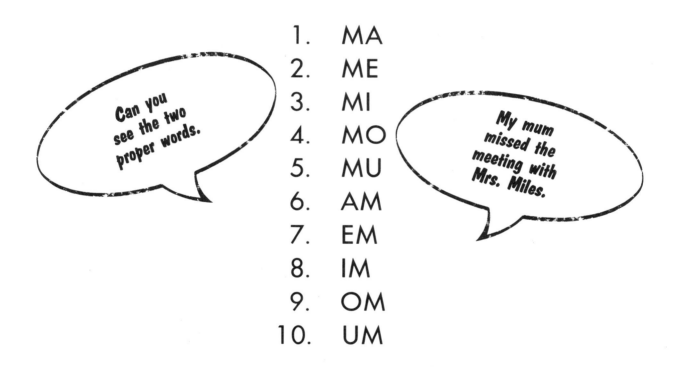

1. MA
2. ME
3. MI
4. MO
5. MU
6. AM
7. EM
8. IM
9. OM
10. UM

Can you see the two proper words.

My mum missed the meeting with Mrs. Miles.

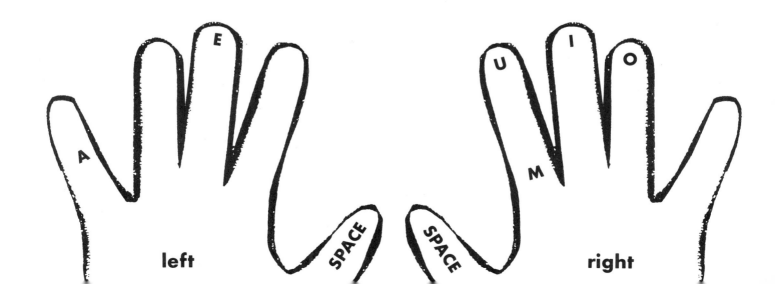

left

SPACE SPACE

right

NINETY-NINE N's

WHAT TO DO: You are going to type at least 99 N's on this page and masses of vowels as well. Type each drill for TWO lines and with TWO spaces.

WARM UP: ("NN" SPACE SPACE)

nn nn nn nn nn nn nn nn nn nn nn nn nn nn nn

nn nn nn nn nn nn nn nn nn nn nn nn nn nn nn

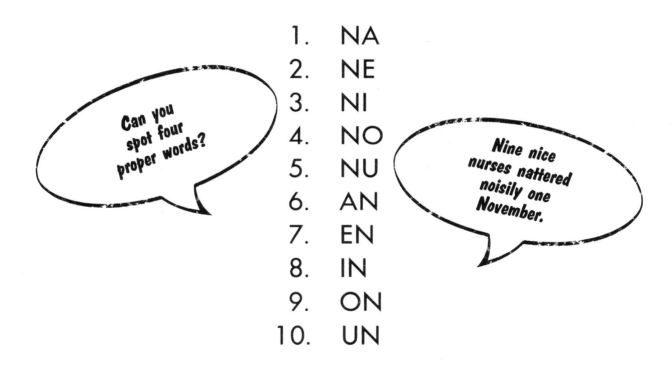

1. NA
2. NE
3. NI
4. NO
5. NU
6. AN
7. EN
8. IN
9. ON
10. UN

Can you spot four proper words?

Nine nice nurses nattered noisily one November.

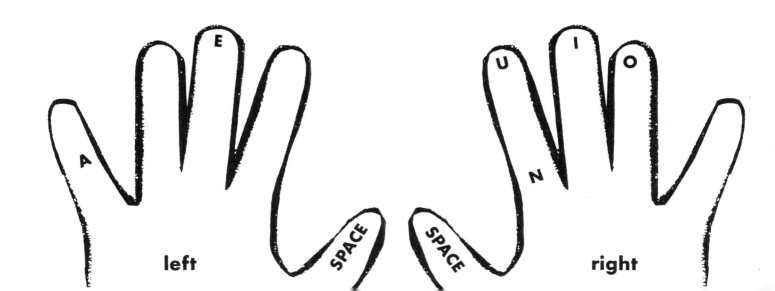

left

right

76

PUT POWER IN "P"

WHAT TO DO: This page will help you get powerful with "P", as well as getting better with the vowels. Type each drill - TWO lines, TWO spaces. Edit out your mistakes.

WARM UP: ("PP" SPACE SPACE)

pp pp pp pp pp pp pp pp pp pp pp pp pp pp
pp pp pp pp pp pp pp pp pp pp pp pp pp pp

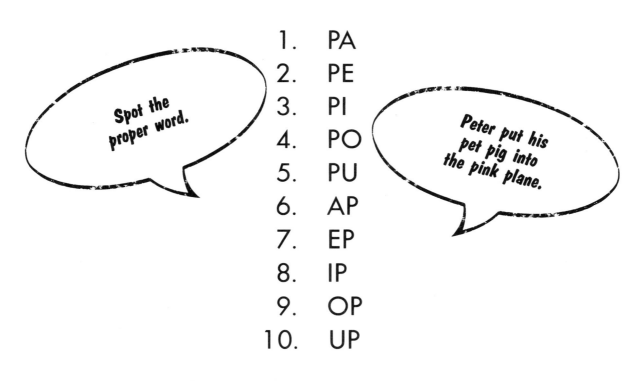

Spot the proper word.

Peter put his pet pig into the pink plane.

1. PA
2. PE
3. PI
4. PO
5. PU
6. AP
7. EP
8. IP
9. OP
10. UP

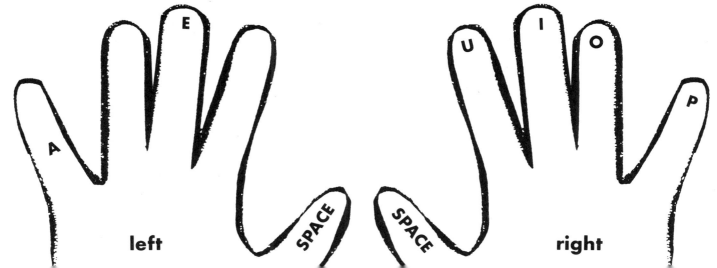

left

right

77

QUICKEN UP "Q"

WHAT TO DO: This page will help you get quick with "Q" and the vowels. Remember that "Q" is always followed by "U" for spelling. Type each exercise for TWO lines with ONE space to make a four beat rhythm.

WARM UP: ("QU" SPACE SPACE)

qu qu qu qu qu qu qu qu qu qu qu qu qu qu
qu qu qu qu qu qu qu qu qu qu qu qu qu qu

1. QUA
2. QUE
3. QUI
4. QUO
5. QUU
6. AQU
7. EQU
8. IQU
9. OQU
10. UQU

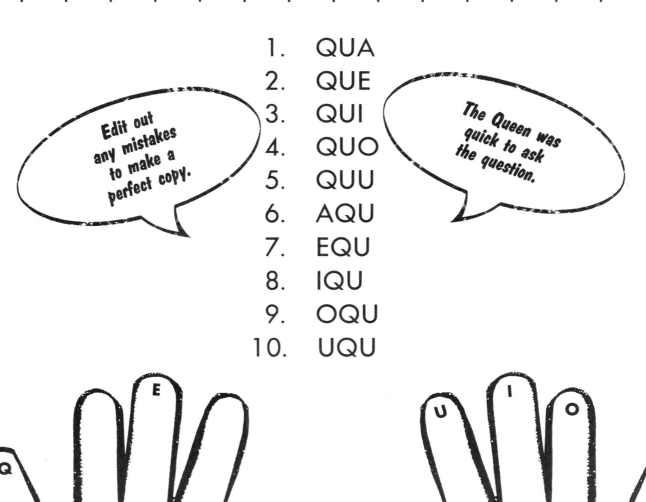

Edit out any mistakes to make a perfect copy.

The Queen was quick to ask the question.

left　　　　　　　　　　right

78

RACE ROUND "R"

WHAT TO DO: Race through this page to learn "R" and also speed up the vowels. Type each drill - TWO lines, TWO spaces. Edit out any problems.

WARM UP: ("RR" SPACE SPACE)

rr rr rr rr rr rr rr rr rr rr rr rr rr rr rr rr rr rr rr
rr rr rr rr rr rr rr rr rr rr rr rr rr rr rr rr rr rr rr

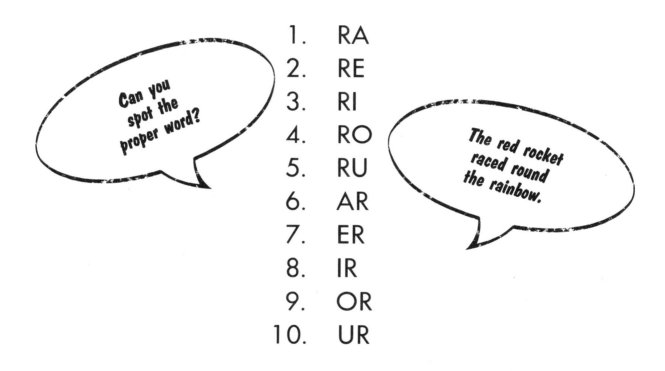

1. RA
2. RE
3. RI
4. RO
5. RU
6. AR
7. ER
8. IR
9. OR
10. UR

Can you spot the proper word?

The red rocket raced round the rainbow.

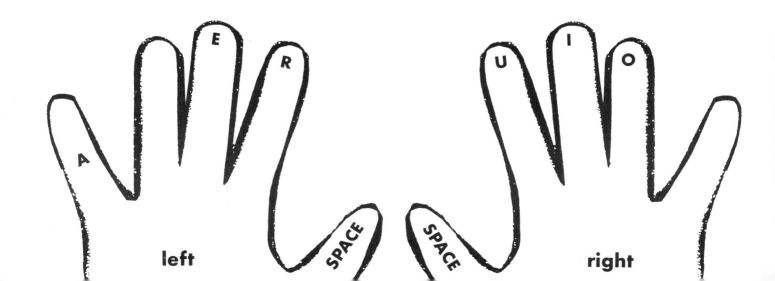

left   right

79

SHARPEN UP "S"

WHAT TO DO: By the end of this page you will be sharp with "S" and faster with the vowels as well. TWO lines, TWO spaces and DELETE any problems.

WARM UP: ("SS" SPACE SPACE)

ss ss ss ss ss ss ss ss ss ss ss ss ss ss ss ss

ss ss ss ss ss ss ss ss ss ss ss ss ss ss ss ss

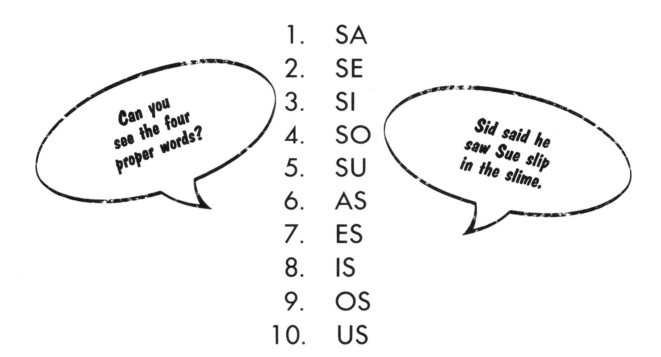

1. SA
2. SE
3. SI
4. SO
5. SU
6. AS
7. ES
8. IS
9. OS
10. US

Can you see the four proper words?

Sid said he saw Sue slip in the slime.

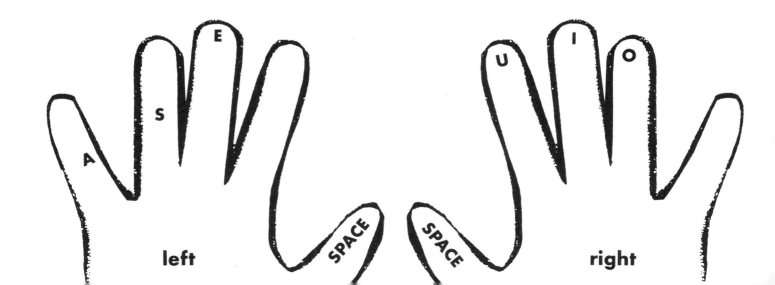

left

SPACE SPACE

right

80

TYPE THE T's

WHAT TO DO: Type the T's and the vowels and learn where they are. Do each drill TWICE with TWO spaces and EDIT out any mistakes you make.

SAMPLE: ("TT" SPACE SPACE)

tt tt tt tt tt tt tt tt tt tt tt tt tt tt tt tt tt tt

tt tt tt tt tt tt tt tt tt tt tt tt tt tt tt tt tt tt

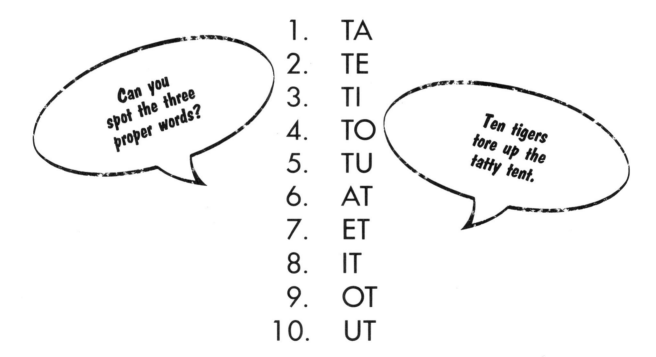

Can you spot the three proper words?

Ten tigers tore up the tatty tent.

1. TA
2. TE
3. TI
4. TO
5. TU
6. AT
7. ET
8. IT
9. OT
10. UT

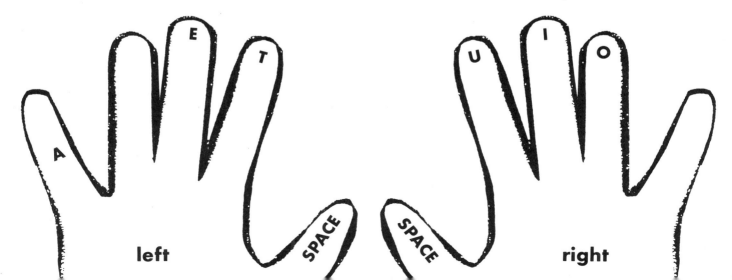

left

right

81

VANQUISH THE "V"s

WHAT TO DO: You will get very good at typing "V" on this page and the vowels as well. TWO lines, and TWO spaces. Edit out any problems.

WARM UP: ("VV" SPACE SPACE)

VV VV VV VV VV VV VV VV VV VV VV VV VV VV VV VV

VV VV VV VV VV VV VV VV VV VV VV VV VV VV VV VV

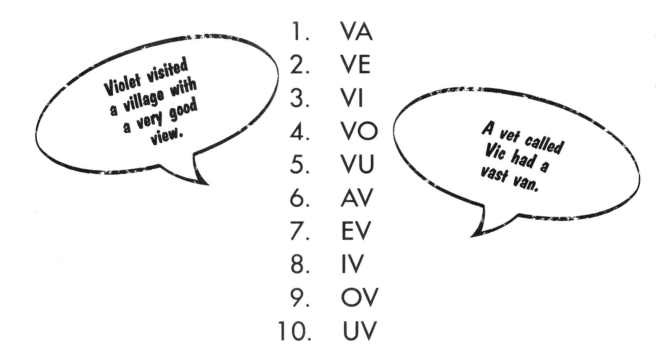

1. VA
2. VE
3. VI
4. VO
5. VU
6. AV
7. EV
8. IV
9. OV
10. UV

Violet visited a village with a very good view.

A vet called Vic had a vast van.

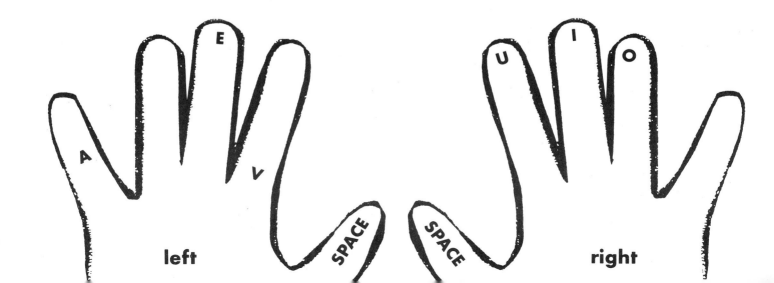

left   right

82

WHIZZ THROUGH "W"

WHAT TO DO: On this page, you will whizz through "W" and the vowels as well. Type each drill for TWO lines, with TWO space and EDIT out errors.

WARM UP: ("WW" SPACE SPACE)

ww ww ww ww ww ww ww ww ww ww ww

ww ww ww ww ww ww ww ww ww ww ww

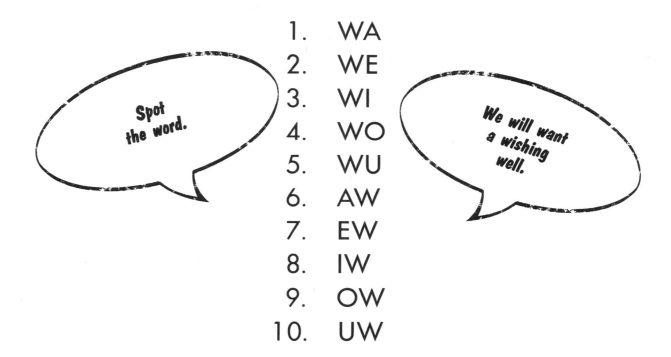

1. WA
2. WE
3. WI
4. WO
5. WU
6. AW
7. EW
8. IW
9. OW
10. UW

Spot the word.

We will want a wishing well.

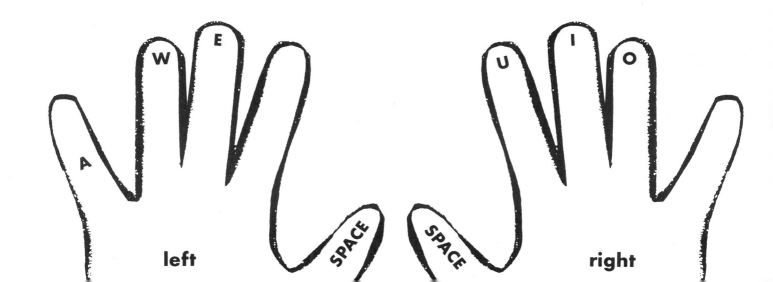

left   SPACE   SPACE   right

83

EXCEL AT "X"

WHAT TO DO: this page will help you excel at typing "X". You will also improve the vowels. Type two letters, with two space, for two lines on each drill Edit out any problems to make a perfect copy.

WARM UP: ("XX" SPACE SPACE)

xx xx xx xx xx xx xx xx xx xx xx xx xx xx xx

xx xx xx xx xx xx xx xx xx xx xx xx xx xx xx

1. XA
2. XE
3. XI
4. XO
5. XU
6. AX
7. EX
8. IX
9. OX
10. UX

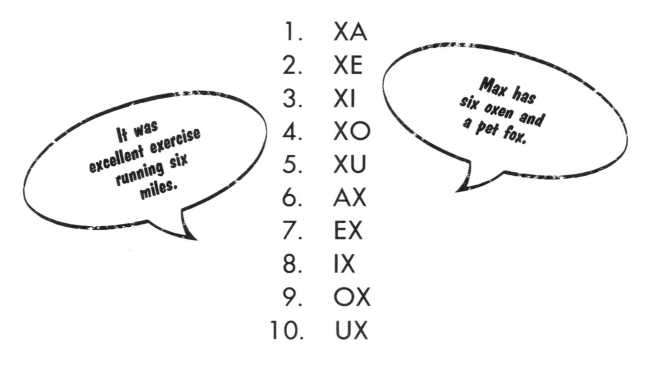

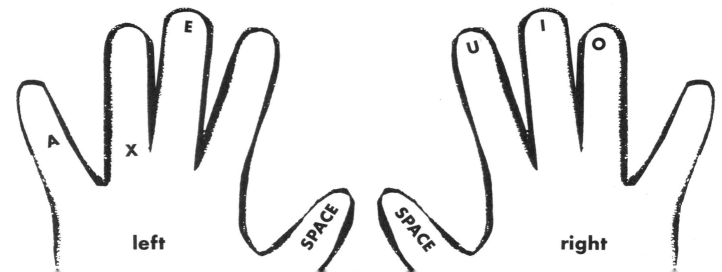

left   right

84

SAY YES TO THE "Y"s

WHAT TO DO: By the end of this page you will be brilliant at typing "Y" and even better at the vowels. Type TWO of everything in the usual way. Make the work perfect by editing out any mistakes.

WARM UP: ("YY" SPACE SPACE)

yy yy yy yy yy yy yy yy yy yy yy yy yy yy yy
yy yy yy yy yy yy yy yy yy yy yy yy yy yy yy

1. YA
2. YE
3. YI
4. YO
5. YU
6. AY
7. EY
8. IY
9. OY
10. UY

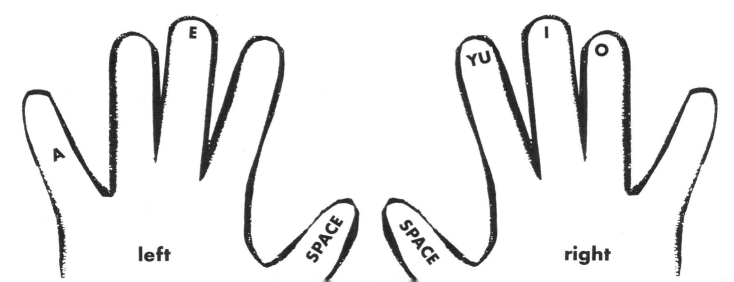

85

ZOOM THROUGH "Z"

WHAT TO DO: You will zoom thorugh "Z" on this page and the vowels as well. Type each drill - TWO lines, TWO spaces - and EDIT out all errors.

WARM UP: ("ZZ" SPACE SPACE)

zz zz zz zz zz zz zz zz zz zz zz zz zz zz zz

zz zz zz zz zz zz zz zz zz zz zz zz zz zz zz

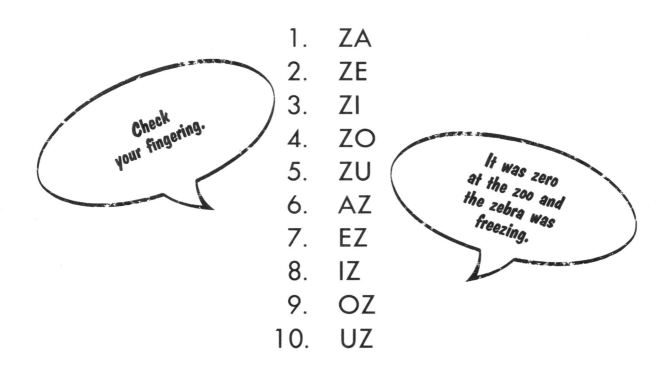

1. ZA
2. ZE
3. ZI
4. ZO
5. ZU
6. AZ
7. EZ
8. IZ
9. OZ
10. UZ

Check your fingering.

It was zero at the zoo and the zebra was freezing.

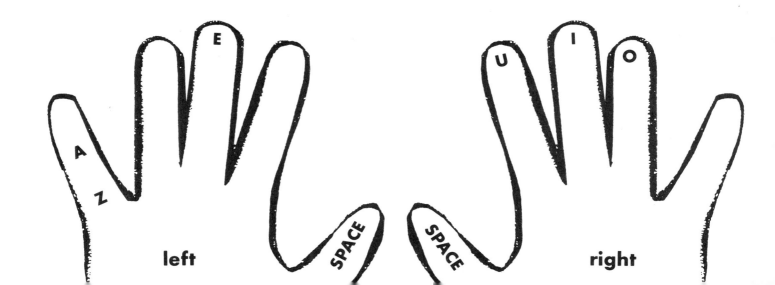

left   right

86

WHAT'S YOUR NAME? (1)

NAME: ROSE BUSH

Copy the exercise.
Use capital letters.
RR space space.

RR RR RR RR RR RR RR RR RR
OO OO OO OO OO OO OO OO OO
SS SS SS SS SS SS SS SS SS
EE EE EE EE EE EE EE EE EE

Use an equidistant font to make the letters line up

Press return 3 times here.

BB BB BB BB BB BB BB BB BB
UU UU UU UU UU UU UU UU UU
SS SS SS SS SS SS SS SS SS
HH HH HH HH HH HH HH HH HH

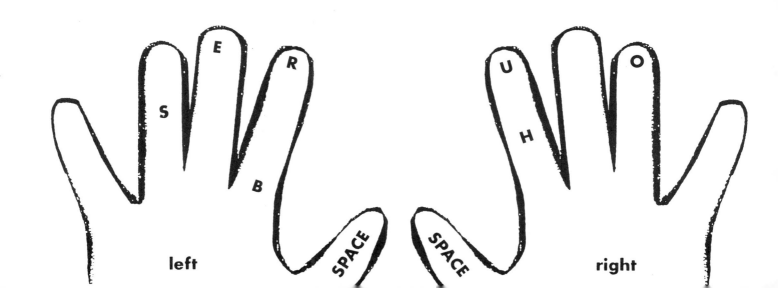

left   SPACE   SPACE   right

87

WHAT'S YOUR NAME? (2)

FIRST NAME: (CAPS) ....

SURNAME: (CAPS) ....

Fill in the Letters of your Name on the Finger Chart.

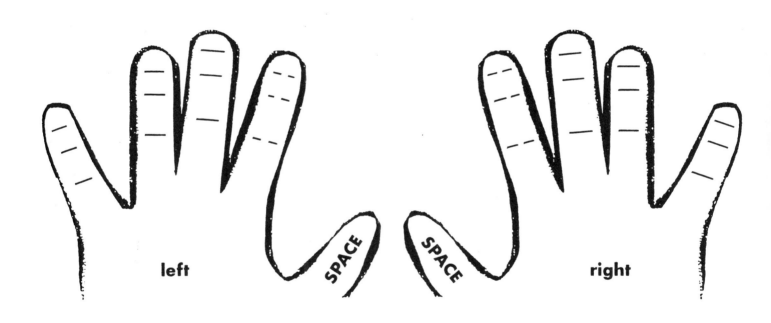

left   SPACE   SPACE   right

Now Type your Name in Columns like the Rose Bush Sheet.

HAPPY CHRISTMAS

WHAT TO DO: Type the exercise below to make HAPPY CHRISTMAS in columns. You will need an equidistant font (see Teacher's Notes Font Choice) to make the letters line up properly.

```
HH  HH  HH  HH  HH  HH  HH  HH  HH
AA  AA  AA  AA  AA  AA  AA  AA  AA
PP  PP  PP  PP  PP  PP  PP  PP  PP
PP  PP  PP  PP  PP  PP  PP  PP  PP
YY  YY  YY  YY  YY  YY  YY  YY  YY
```

You can make up any messages and display them in this way. Try some others.

3 line gap here.

```
CC  CC  CC  CC  CC  CC  CC  CC  CC
HH  HH  HH  HH  HH  HH  HH  HH  HH
RR  RR  RR  RR  RR  RR  RR  RR  RR
II  II  II  II  II  II  II  II  II
SS  SS  SS  SS  SS  SS  SS  SS  SS
TT  TT  TT  TT  TT  TT  TT  TT  TT
MM  MM  MM  MM  MM  MM  MM  MM  MM
AA  AA  AA  AA  AA  AA  AA  AA  AA
SS  SS  SS  SS  SS  SS  SS  SS  SS
```

Fill in the letters you will need for "HAPPY CHRISTMAS"

left   SPACE SPACE   right

89

THE ALPHABET TREE

WHAT TO DO: This exercise gives extra practice in using every keyboard letter. Work out the fingering and fill the letters in on the chart – the first ones have been done for you. Use your CENTRE function to make the tree shape. A guide to the number of letters you need is on the right hand side. You need an equidistant font (see Teacher's Notes Font Choice) for the lines to centre properly in the tree shape.

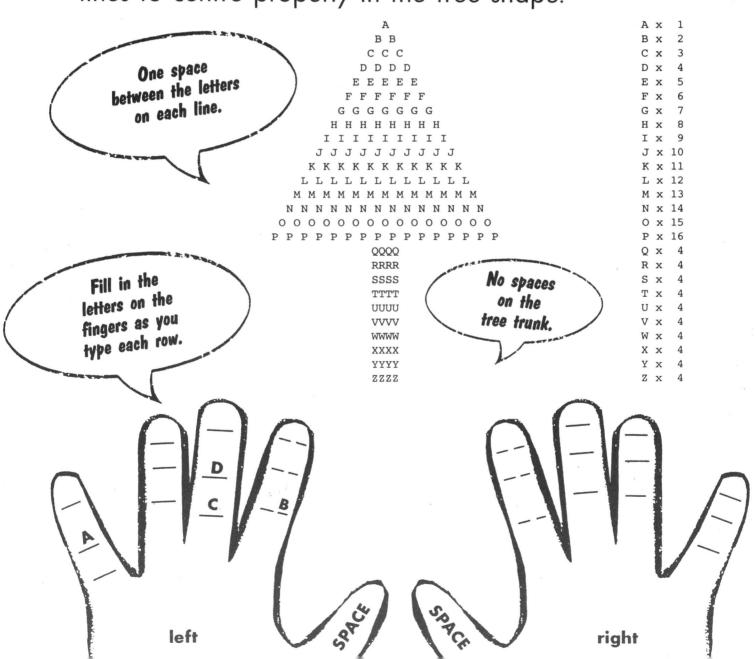

```
                    A                    A  x   1
                   B B                   B  x   2
                  C C C                   C  x   3
                 D D D D                  D  x   4
                E E E E E                 E  x   5
               F F F F F F                F  x   6
              G G G G G G G               G  x   7
             H H H H H H H H              H  x   8
            I I I I I I I I I             I  x   9
           J J J J J J J J J J            J  x  10
          K K K K K K K K K K K           K  x  11
         L L L L L L L L L L L L          L  x  12
        M M M M M M M M M M M M M         M  x  13
       N N N N N N N N N N N N N N        N  x  14
      O O O O O O O O O O O O O O O       O  x  15
     P P P P P P P P P P P P P P P P      P  x  16
                 QQQQ                     Q  x   4
                 RRRR                     R  x   4
                 SSSS                     S  x   4
                 TTTT                     T  x   4
                 UUUU                     U  x   4
                 VVVV                     V  x   4
                 WWWW                     W  x   4
                 XXXX                     X  x   4
                 YYYY                     Y  x   4
                 ZZZZ                     Z  x   4
```

One space between the letters on each line.

Fill in the letters on the fingers as you type each row.

No spaces on the tree trunk.

left   SPACE   SPACE   right